# CHILD CARE
## *and* EDUCATION

### NVQ/SVQ LEVEL 2 WORKBOOK

## CACHE

### COUNCIL FOR AWARDS IN CHILDREN'S CARE AND EDUCATION
(Incorporating CEYA and the NNEB)

## Hodder & Stoughton

A MEMBER OF THE HODDER HEADLINE GROUP

*British Library Cataloguing in Publication Data*

A catalogue for this title is available from the British Library.

ISBN 0 340 64333 1

First published 1995
Impression number   10  9  8  7  6  5  4  3  2  1
Year                1999  1998  1997  1996  1995

Typeset by Wearset, Boldon, Tyne and Wear.
Printed in Great Britain for Hodder & Stoughton Educational, a division of Hodder Headline Plc, 338 Euston Road, London NW1 3BH by The Bath Press, Avon.

# CONTENTS

# INTRODUCTION

This workbook is designed to help you to provide evidence of your underpinning knowledge and understanding of child care and education in NVQ/SVQ at level 2. The Workbook is divided into 16 units. Each unit contains a variety of different tasks and portfolio activities which will help you to show your knowledge and understanding of child care and education at NVQ Level 2.

The first eight units form the core of NVQ Level 2 Child Care and Education. These are called:

| | |
|---|---|
| C.2 | Care for children's physical needs |
| C.4 | Support children's social and emotional development |
| C.6 | Contribute to the management of children's behaviour |
| C.8 | Set out and clear away play activities |
| C.9 | Work with young children |
| E.1 | Maintain a child orientated environment |
| E.2 | Maintain the safety of children |
| P.2 | Establish and maintain relationships with parents of young children |

The remaining eight units in the workbook provide tasks which cover the endorsement units.

*Endorsement A    Work with Babies*
| | |
|---|---|
| C.12 | Feed babies |
| C.13 | Care for babies |

*Endorsement B    Work in Support of Others*
| | |
|---|---|
| M.1 | Give administrative and technical support on request |
| M.3 | Work under the direction of others |

*Endorsement C    Work in a Pre-school Group*
| | |
|---|---|
| P.9 | Work with parents in a group for young children |
| M.2 | Carry out the administration of the provision for a care/education setting |

*Endorsement D    Work in a Community-Run Pre-School Group*
| | |
|---|---|
| P.9 | Work with parents in a group for young children |
| M.20 | Work with/to a management committee |

(**NB:** The tasks for P.9 are not repeated for Endorsement C and D.)

**REMEMBER**
If you are using the materials in this workbook for assessment purposes for the NVQ/SVQ

Level 2, it is important to discuss your work with your assessor as he/she may require further evidence of your understanding of a unit. You may also find that some tasks overlap. It is not necessary to repeat the work.

At the end of each Progress Checklist you will find a sample of books that you may find helpful when answering the questions. CACHE does not endorse any particular books for the NVQ/SVQ Level 2 Child Care and Education.

# ACKNOWLEDGEMENTS

CACHE would like to thank Alison Mitchell and other members of the Curriculum and Assessment department for their invaluable contribution to this workbook.

# PORTFOLIO ACTIVITIES

As you progress through the workbook you will be asked to complete portfolio activities. These are practical tasks which should relate to your work setting, if possible. The activities include observations of children, planning activities for children, designing posters, preparing booklets or leaflets to explain information to staff and/or parents.

It is important that you store your portfolio activities in a safe place as you may want to have the materials assessed for the NVQ/SVQ in Child Care and Education. You may find it helpful to use an A4 file for this. If you do, then these guidelines may be of value to you:

- Write your name and address clearly at the beginning of the file. (This may be invaluable if you leave your file on the bus!)
- If you are working with young children, describe your place of work and the age range of the children you are working with. Do not name the work setting or the staff with whom you work or the name of the child or family. It is important to retain confidentiality at all times.
- Begin a contents page. This can be very useful when trying to find specific activities.
- Use dividers to separate individual units.
- Number the pages of your file.
- Begin to compile a references and bibliography section. It is always important to note the title, author, date of publication and publisher of any books or articles you have referred to as you have worked on your answers. However, do not be tempted to leave it until you have finished the workbook. You will never be able to find the information and it will become an extremely boring and time-consuming task.

## *Recording your portfolio activities*

When writing up your portfolio activities you should provide as much information as possible. It should include:

- The criteria number, eg C.2.4.b.
- The aim of the activity, eg To observe the rest and sleep patterns of a child.
- Details of preparation and resources required.
- The starting and finishing time of the observation.
- The number of adults and children present during the activity.
- The first names of the child/children or other identification, eg first letter of the child's name.
- A brief description of the child/children including details of age, gender and other relevant information.
- Details on how effective the activity/observation was.
- How the information gained helps with future work with children and families.

# *Progress Checklist*

Throughout the workbook you will find progress checklists. These will help you to plan your work and monitor your progress. Three age groups are identified for each of the activities. You should aim to provide activities and/or observations for each of the age groups, if possible. When you are assessed for your NVQ/SVQ, you will be required to demonstrate a knowledge and understanding across each of the age ranges.

## USEFUL BOOKS

*Take a Look: Observation and Portfolio Assessment in Early Childhood.* S. Martin (1994) Addison-Wesley Publishers.

*Seeing Young Children: A Guide for Observing and Recording Behaviour.* W. Bentzen (1993) Delmar.

# WHAT SHOULD I DO NOW?

Follow the seven steps given below to help you complete the workbook.

**Step 1** READ
**Step 2**       DISCUSS
**Step 3**           CHOOSE
**Step 4**              RESEARCH
**Step 5**                 OBSERVE
**Step 6**                    RECORD
**Step 7**                       ASSESSMENT

**Step 1** Choose the unit that you would like to start with. It may be a topic that you are particularly interested in or one that you are familiar with. Read through the unit carefully before you begin to fill in the answers. Do not be tempted to start answering questions straight away as you may give yourself a lot of additional work.

**Step 2** If you have a mentor or tutor, discuss the content of the unit with him/her. Your mentor or tutor will help you to plan a programme of work. If you do not have a mentor or tutor it may be useful to complete a programme of work such as the one started on p. 4 for Unit C.2. A separate one would need to be completed for each unit.

**Step 3** Choose an appropriate section to start with. You do not have to start at the beginning of every section.

**Step 4** Begin to gather information. This will mean visiting the library, reading appropriate articles in magazines and books, and visiting local government offices etc.

**Step 5** Observe and record any appropriate information. You may want to take photographs of the work you are doing to include in your portfolio. If you do take photographs, remember to ask permission.

**Step 6** When you feel you have gathered all the necessary information and you understand the work, you should then complete the relevant section in the unit. Additional work should be clearly named and attached to your unit.

**Step 7** When you have finished the unit, read over your work again and make sure that you have included all the relevant information. When you are satisfied with your work, you are then ready to go on to the next unit.

# Example programme of work

This is the sort of programme of work you should aim to complete for each unit. These notes will help you to see at a glance what needs to be done for each criteria, so helping you to cover all aspects effectively without wasting time or doubling up on information.

| Unit | Criteria | Notes |
|------|----------|-------|
| C.2 | C.2.1.a | Visit your local library for information on the nutritional value of foods. Local health stores may have leaflets. Information may be useful for C.2.1.b |
| | | |
| | | |
| | | |
| | | |
| | | |
| | | |
| | | |
| | | |

# C.2 CARE FOR CHILDREN'S PHYSICAL NEEDS UNIT WIDE KNOWLEDGE

| | Criteria | Knowledge evidence | Date completed |
|---|---|---|---|
| PROGRESS CHECKLIST | C.2.a | Basic knowledge of children's development 6 weeks to 8 years and how provision for their physical needs affects their development. | |
| | C.2.b | The development and recognition of socially accepted behaviour and ability to understand and comply with socially accepted norms. | |
| | C.2.c | Variation in cultural and religious practices and customs and their implication for caring for children's physical needs. | |
| | C.2.d | Stereotypical assumptions in assessing and providing for children's physical needs and how to avoid/challenge them. | |
| | C.2.e | Health and safety requirements relevant to the setting and how to obtain further advice. | |
| | C.2.f | Methods and techniques for communicating with young children and adults including verbal and non-verbal communication. | |
| | C.2.g | The boundaries of confidentiality for the setting and how, when and to whom information can be passed. | |

## USEFUL BOOKS

*Special Issues in Child Care.* M. O'Hagan and M. Smith (1993) Bailliere Tindall.
*Babies and Young Children Book 1 Development 0–7 years.* Beaver *et al* (1994) Stanley Thornes.
*Caring for the under 8s.* Jennie and Lance Lindon (1993) Macmillan.
*The Developing Child* (5th ed.). Helen Bee (1989) Harper Collins.

| PORTFOLIO ACTIVITY SUMMARY | | | | |
| --- | --- | --- | --- | --- |
| **Criteria** | **Portfolio page reference** | **0–1** | **1–4** | **4–7** |
| C.2.a | See page 7 for Portfolio Activity | | | |
| C.2.e | See page 9 for Portfolio Activity | | | |

# C.2 Care for children's physical needs

### C.2.a Portfolio Activity

*Design a booklet for parents which explains the physical development of a young child aged 6 weeks to 7 years 11 months.*

C.2.b    How can a child be encouraged to understand what socially acceptable behaviour is?

........................................................................................

........................................................................................

........................................................................................

........................................................................................

........................................................................................

How can socially acceptable behaviour be encouraged?

........................................................................................

........................................................................................

........................................................................................

........................................................................................

........................................................................................

C.2.c    Why is it important for the child care and education worker to consider the cultural and religious practices of the children in his/her care?

........................................................................................

........................................................................................

..............................................................................................................

..............................................................................................................

..............................................................................................................

..............................................................................................................

What implications could these differences have on a child's physical needs?

..............................................................................................................

..............................................................................................................

..............................................................................................................

..............................................................................................................

..............................................................................................................

..............................................................................................................

C.2.d    What stereotypical assumptions could be made when providing for children's physical needs? Give TWO assumptions.

..............................................................................................................

..............................................................................................................

..............................................................................................................

..............................................................................................................

For EACH of the above assumptions, describe a way in which it could be avoided and/or challenged.

..............................................................................................................

..............................................................................................................

..............................................................................................................

..............................................................................................................

## C.2.e Portfolio Activity

*Collect information which explains the health and safety regulations of the work setting.*

C.2.f    Describe how an adult can communicate with a young child by means of:

(*a*) verbal communication;

.......................................................................................................................

.......................................................................................................................

.......................................................................................................................

.......................................................................................................................

.......................................................................................................................

(*b*) non-verbal communication.

.......................................................................................................................

.......................................................................................................................

.......................................................................................................................

.......................................................................................................................

.......................................................................................................................

C.2.g    Why is it important to maintain confidentiality in the work setting?

.......................................................................................................................

.......................................................................................................................

What information should be shared with other members of staff?

.......................................................................................................................

Who should confidential information be available to?

.......................................................................................................................

.......................................................................................................................

.......................................................................................................................

# C.2.1 Provide food and drinks for children

<table>
<tr><td rowspan="11" style="writing-mode: vertical-lr">PROGRESS CHECKLIST</td><td>Criteria</td><td>Knowledge evidence</td><td>Date completed</td></tr>
<tr><td>C.2.1.a</td><td>The nutritional value of common foodstuffs and drinks and what constitutes a balanced diet.</td><td></td></tr>
<tr><td>C.2.1.b</td><td>The nutritional value in relation to size of portions and methods of preparation.</td><td></td></tr>
<tr><td>C.2.1.c</td><td>Ways of presenting food and drink that are attractive to children and easy to manage.</td><td></td></tr>
<tr><td>C.2.1.d</td><td>Health and safety requirements in relation to food preparation and storage.</td><td></td></tr>
<tr><td>C.2.1.e</td><td>Common dietary requirements associated with religious and cultural practices.</td><td></td></tr>
<tr><td>C.2.1.f</td><td>The importance of valuing and introducing to children cultural and religious variations in types of food, types of preparation and utensils and eating habits.</td><td></td></tr>
<tr><td>C.2.1.g</td><td>The role of food in social and cultural life and in shaping attitudes and behaviour.</td><td></td></tr>
<tr><td>C.2.1.h</td><td>The variety of food preferences and eating habits children may have and the way they may change over time.</td><td></td></tr>
<tr><td>C.2.1.i</td><td>Common food allergies and implications for diets.</td><td></td></tr>
<tr><td>C.2.1.j</td><td>Effects of illness and emotional disturbance on appetite.</td><td></td></tr>
</table>

## USEFUL BOOKS

*Essential Food Hygiene.* Dr R. J. Donaldson (1991) Royal Society of Health.
*Food and Nutrition.* A. Tull (1993) Oxford University Press.
*The Nursery Food Book.* M. Whiting and J. Lobstein (1992) Edward Arnold.

| PORTFOLIO ACTIVITY SUMMARY | | | | |
|---|---|---|---|---|
| **Criteria** | **Portfolio page reference** | **0–1** | **1–4** | **4–7** |
| C.2.1.a | See below for Portfolio Activity | | | |
| C.2.1.h | See page 15 for Portfolio Activity | | | |

C.2.1.a    Select ONE food from EACH category below and describe the nutritional value of that food.

| **A** | **B** | **C** | **D** |
|---|---|---|---|
| Bread | Cheese | Oranges | Milk |
| Pasta | Meat | Carrots | Liver |

.................................................................................................................

.................................................................................................................

.................................................................................................................

.................................................................................................................

.................................................................................................................

.................................................................................................................

.................................................................................................................

.................................................................................................................

### *C.2.1.a Portfolio Activity*

*Plan and prepare ONE meal and ONE snack which meet the nutritional requirements of a child. The appropriate menus should be included. Explain how effective your planning and preparation have been in meeting the needs of the child.*

C.2.1.b    Describe how the following methods of preparation affect the nutritional value of food.

(*a*) frying;

.................................................................................................................

.................................................................................................................

(*b*) steaming;

..................................................................................................................................

..................................................................................................................................

(*c*) chopping.

..................................................................................................................................

..................................................................................................................................


C.2.1.c    Describe how the child care and education worker can present food AND
drink to the child which would encourage him/her to eat and drink.

..................................................................................................................................

..................................................................................................................................

..................................................................................................................................

..................................................................................................................................

..................................................................................................................................

..................................................................................................................................


C.2.1.d    Describe how the child care and education worker can safely and hygienically:

(*a*) prepare food;

..................................................................................................................................

..................................................................................................................................

..................................................................................................................................

..................................................................................................................................

..................................................................................................................................

..................................................................................................................................

(*b*)  store food;

..............................................................................................................................................

..............................................................................................................................................

..............................................................................................................................................

..............................................................................................................................................

..............................................................................................................................................

..............................................................................................................................................

(*c*)  provide eating areas.

..............................................................................................................................................

..............................................................................................................................................

..............................................................................................................................................

..............................................................................................................................................

..............................................................................................................................................

..............................................................................................................................................

List FIVE health and safety requirements in relation to food preparation.

..............................................................................................................................................

..............................................................................................................................................

..............................................................................................................................................

..............................................................................................................................................

List FIVE health and safety requirements in relation to storage of food.

..............................................................................................................................................

..............................................................................................................................................

..................................................................................................

..................................................................................................

..................................................................................................

C.2.1.e    Name THREE religions with different dietary requirements. For EACH
religion list the main dietary requirements.

..................................................................................................

..................................................................................................

..................................................................................................

C.2.1.f    Why is it important to encourage children to value the food and eating habits
of children from other religions and cultures?

..................................................................................................

..................................................................................................

..................................................................................................

..................................................................................................

..................................................................................................

..................................................................................................

C.2.1.g    Describe the role of food in social and cultural life.

..................................................................................................

..................................................................................................

..................................................................................................

..................................................................................................

What effect can different types of food have on a child's attitude and
behaviour?

..................................................................................................

..................................................................................................................................

..................................................................................................................................

..................................................................................................................................

### C.2.1.h Portfolio Activity

*Observe and record the eating habits and food likes and dislikes of a child.*

C.2.1.i    Name TWO food allergies common to children. For EACH allergy, name THREE nutrients that are missing from the child's diet and explain what the child care and education worker can do to overcome this difficulty.

(*a*) Food allergy    ...............................................................................................

(i) ...........................................................................................

(ii) ..........................................................................................

(iii) .........................................................................................

(*b*) Food allergy    ...............................................................................................

(i) ...........................................................................................

(ii) ..........................................................................................

(iii) .........................................................................................

C.2.1.j    Describe the effects that illness may have on a child's appetite.

..................................................................................................................................

..................................................................................................................................

..................................................................................................................................

..................................................................................................................................

..................................................................................................................................

..................................................................................................................................

# C.2.2 Contribute to children's personal hygiene

<table>
<tr><td rowspan="8" style="writing-mode: vertical-rl">PROGRESS CHECKLIST</td><td>Criteria</td><td>Knowledge evidence</td><td>Date completed</td></tr>
<tr><td>C.2.2.a</td><td>The general health and hygiene requirements of young children and what constitute appropriate personal hygiene routines.</td><td></td></tr>
<tr><td>C.2.2.b</td><td>The purpose, application and storage of toiletries, cleaning materials and equipment.</td><td></td></tr>
<tr><td>C.2.2.c</td><td>The cause of cross-infection and procedures to prevent cross-infection.</td><td></td></tr>
<tr><td>C.2.2.d</td><td>The procedures for dealing with waste products.</td><td></td></tr>
<tr><td>C.2.2.e</td><td>The methods of caring for the personal hygiene of young children and how these may vary with family/cultural background, skin and hair types, and across child care settings.</td><td></td></tr>
<tr><td>C.2.2.f</td><td>The ways in which toilet training and hygiene routines are said to shape attitudes and behaviour.</td><td></td></tr>
<tr><td>C.2.2.g</td><td>Signs of infection, abrasions and other abnormalities including variation from normal stools and urine and their significance.</td><td></td></tr>
</table>

## USEFUL BOOKS

*Babies and Young Children Book 1 Development 0–7 years.* Beaver *et al;* (1994) Stanley Thornes.

| PORTFOLIO ACTIVITY SUMMARY | | | | |
|---|---|---|---|---|
| **Criteria** | **Portfolio page reference** | **0–1** | **1–4** | **4–7** |
| C.2.2.a | See page 17 for Portfolio Activity | | | |
| C.2.2.e | See page 19 for Portfolio Activity | | | |

### C.2.2.a Portfolio Activity

*Plan a personal hygiene routine for a child aged between 1–4 years and 4–7 years. It should include:*

    (*a*) *hand washing;*

    (*b*) *care of skin and hair;*

    (*c*) *care of teeth*

C.2.2.b    Name TWO toiletries and TWO cleaning materials that would be used in the work setting to promote hygiene. Also, name TWO pieces of equipment that would be used by the child care and education worker when encouraging a child's personal hygiene routine. For each item, describe:

(*a*) the purpose of the item;
(*b*) how it is applied or used;
(*c*) how it would be stored.

Toiletries

    1(a) .......................................................................................................................................

      (b) .......................................................................................................................................

      (c) .......................................................................................................................................

    2(a) .......................................................................................................................................

      (b) .......................................................................................................................................

      (c) .......................................................................................................................................

Cleaning materials

    1(a) .......................................................................................................................................

      (b) .......................................................................................................................................

      (c) .......................................................................................................................................

    2(a) .......................................................................................................................................

      (b) .......................................................................................................................................

      (c) .......................................................................................................................................

Equipment

1(a) .............................................................................................................................

(b) .............................................................................................................................

(c) .............................................................................................................................

2(a) .............................................................................................................................

(b) .............................................................................................................................

(c) .............................................................................................................................

C.2.2.c    Describe what causes cross-infection AND how it can be prevented in the work setting.

.................................................................................................................................

.................................................................................................................................

.................................................................................................................................

.................................................................................................................................

.................................................................................................................................

.................................................................................................................................

.................................................................................................................................

.................................................................................................................................

.................................................................................................................................

.................................................................................................................................

.................................................................................................................................

C.2.2.d    How should the following waste products be disposed of safely and hygienically?

(*a*) disposable nappies;

.......................................................................................................................

.......................................................................................................................

(*b*) paper towels;

.......................................................................................................................

.......................................................................................................................

(*c*) food scraps.

.......................................................................................................................

.......................................................................................................................

## *C.2.2.e Portfolio Activity*

*Plan and implement ONE activity which encourages the personal hygiene of a child. Explain how effective you have been in encouraging the personal hygiene of the child.*

C.2.2.f    Describe how toilet training and personal hygiene routines can influence a child's attitude and behaviour.

.......................................................................................................................

.......................................................................................................................

.......................................................................................................................

.......................................................................................................................

C.2.2.g    List FIVE examples of the signs of infection and any other unusual symptoms that a child may have.

.......................................................................................................................

.......................................................................................................................

.......................................................................................................................

.......................................................................................................................

.......................................................................................................................

# C.2.3 Respond to illness in a child

| | Criteria | Knowledge evidence | Date completed |
|---|---|---|---|
| **PROGRESS CHECKLIST** | C.2.3.a | Symptoms of commonly encountered illnesses and methods of dealing with them. | |
| | C.2.3.b | The significance and criticality of symptoms in relation to age/development of children. | |
| | C.2.3.c | Importance of keeping records of significant medical conditions and of medication administered. | |
| | C.2.3.d | Sources of help in identification and response to symptoms. | |
| | C.2.3.e | The legal requirements re parental consent to administration of medicines, creams, lotions, dressings and reporting of communicable diseases. | |
| | C.2.3.f | Procedures for dealing with a child who is unconscious. | |
| | C.2.3.g | The recognition of symptoms in children of varying skin tones. | |
| | C.2.3.h | Children's emotional needs when unwell and the effects of illness on subsequent behaviour. | |
| | C.2.3.i | Storage requirements and need for proper labelling of medicines. | |
| | C.2.3.j | Parents' emotional needs and own role when children are taken ill. | |
| | C.2.3.k | Implications of chronic medical conditions for the child's care. | |
| | C.2.3.l | When, how and to whom to record and report incidents. | |

# USEFUL BOOKS

*Special Issues in Child Care.* M. O'Hagan and M. Smith (1993) Bailliere Tindall.

| PORTFOLIO ACTIVITY SUMMARY | | 0–1 | 1–4 | 4–7 |
|---|---|---|---|---|
| **Criteria** | **Portfolio page reference** | | | |
| C.2.3.b | See page 22 for Portfolio Activity | | | |
| C.2.3.c | See page 22 for Portfolio Activity | | | |
| C.2.3.k | See page 24 for Portfolio Activity | | | |

C.2.3.a  Name TWO symptoms for each of the childhood illnesses listed below.

(*a*) chicken pox;

..............................................................................................................

..............................................................................................................

(*b*) measles;

..............................................................................................................

..............................................................................................................

(*c*) meningitis;

..............................................................................................................

..............................................................................................................

(*d*) rubella.

..............................................................................................................

..............................................................................................................

Choose ONE of the illnesses above and describe how the child care and education worker can care for the child.

..............................................................................................................

..............................................................................................................

..............................................................................................................

C.2.3.b    Why is it important to respond quickly when you suspect that a child may be ill?

.......................................................................................................................

.......................................................................................................................

 ### C.2.3.b Portfolio Activity

*Describe an occasion when you responded to a child who became ill. Explain how effective you were in coping with the situation.*

C.2.3.c    Why is it important to keep records of medical illnesses and of the medicines given?

.......................................................................................................................

.......................................................................................................................

.......................................................................................................................

.......................................................................................................................

### C.2.3.c Portfolio Activity

*EITHER record an ill child's state of health and any changes in his/her condition OR design a record sheet that could be used in the work setting to monitor a child's state of health.*

C.2.3.d    Where could the child care and education worker get help in identifying and responding to symptoms? Name THREE resources.

.......................................................................................................................

.......................................................................................................................

.......................................................................................................................

C.2.3.e    Describe the procedures that the work setting uses for the following:

(*a*) administering medicines, creams, lotions, dressings;

.......................................................................................................................

.......................................................................................................................

(*b*) storing and labelling of medicines.

......................................................................................................

......................................................................................................

C.2.3.f    In order of priority, list the care that should be given to an unconscious child.

1
......................................................................................................
2
......................................................................................................
3
......................................................................................................
4
......................................................................................................
5
......................................................................................................

C.2.3.g    Describe TWO difficulties that the child care and education worker may have in recognising illness in children with varying skin tones.

......................................................................................................

......................................................................................................

......................................................................................................

......................................................................................................

C.2.3.h    Describe the emotional needs of a child who is ill AND explain how it may affect his/her behaviour.

......................................................................................................

......................................................................................................

......................................................................................................

......................................................................................................

......................................................................................................

......................................................................................................

C.2.3.j   What are the emotional needs of a parent when a child is ill?

..................................................................................................................

..................................................................................................................

..................................................................................................................

..................................................................................................................

What is the role of the child care and education worker when a child is ill?

..................................................................................................................

..................................................................................................................

..................................................................................................................

..................................................................................................................

..................................................................................................................

C.2.3.k   The chronically ill child may need special care. Describe TWO ways in which the child care and education worker can care for the child.

..................................................................................................................

..................................................................................................................

..................................................................................................................

..................................................................................................................

## C.2.3.k Portfolio Activity

*Design a chart for staff in the work setting explaining when, how and to whom to record and report incidents.*

# C.2.4 Provide opportunities for children to rest or sleep

| PROGRESS CHECKLIST | Criteria | Knowledge evidence | Date completed |
|---|---|---|---|
| | C.2.4.a | The importance of rest/sleep or quiet periods as part of the daily routine and at matching the routines of home and child care setting. | |
| | C.2.4.b | The variation of rest and sleep requirements of children at different ages and as individuals. | |
| | C.2.4.c | How to use space and equipment to promote opportunities for rest and/or sleep. | |
| | C.2.4.d | Methods of managing conflict between children in choice of rest or activity. | |
| | C.2.4.e | The variation in approaches to informal/formal bedtimes adopted by families of different background. | |
| | C.2.4.f | The problems for families when the requirements for a child's rest/sleep pattern does not match the family's evening life style. | |

## USEFUL BOOKS

The unit wide knowledge books will help you in this section.

| PORTFOLIO ACTIVITY SUMMARY | | | | |
|---|---|---|---|---|
| Criteria | Portfolio page reference | 0–1 | 1–4 | 4–7 |
| C.2.4.b | See page 26 for Portfolio Activity | | | |
| C.2.4.c | See page 26 for Portfolio Activity | | | |

C.2.4.a    Why is it important for children to have time to rest or have a quiet time
during the day?

..................................................................................................................................

..................................................................................................................................

..................................................................................................................................

..................................................................................................................................

..................................................................................................................................

### C.2.4.b Portfolio Activity

*Observe a child at regular intervals throughout the day. Note the rest or sleep pattern of the child.*
*Observe the sleep or rest pattern of a child of a different age. Compare the children's different needs for*
*rest and/or sleep.*

### C.2.4.c Portfolio Activity

*Describe how the work setting uses its space and equipment to allow the children to have time for rest*
*and/or sleep.*

C.2.4.d    Describe how a child care and education worker would deal with a child who
did not want to rest or sleep.

..................................................................................................................................

..................................................................................................................................

..................................................................................................................................

..................................................................................................................................

..................................................................................................................................

C.2.4.e    Describe how bedtime routines may vary in different families and why.

..................................................................................................................................

..........................................................................................................................

..........................................................................................................................

..........................................................................................................................

**C.2.4.f**    What difficulties may arise for a family when a child does not have a regular
sleep pattern?

..........................................................................................................................

..........................................................................................................................

..........................................................................................................................

..........................................................................................................................

# C.2.5 *Provide opportunities for children's exercise*

| | Criteria | Knowledge evidence | Date completed |
|---|---|---|---|
| **PROGRESS CHECKLIST** | C.2.5.a | The general role of exercise in promoting physical growth and development. | |
| | C.2.5.b | The importance of adequate supervision for children during physical exercise. | |
| | C.2.5.c | The relationship between level of child's development and physical abilities and appropriate exercise. | |
| | C.2.5.d | How to undertake simple adaptations to equipment and spatial arrangement of equipment to suit children's needs and safety requirements. | |
| | C.2.5.e | Indicators of stereotypical approaches to exercise and how to provide non-stereotypical exercise and play. | |
| | C.2.5.f | Methods of providing for different types of exercise and physical play. | |
| | C.2.5.g | The role of physical achievement in developing self-confidence. | |

## USEFUL BOOKS

*Caring for the Under 8s.* Jennie and Lance Lindon (1993) Macmillan.
*Helping Children to Learn Through a Movement Perspective.* Mollie Davies (1995) Hodder and Stoughton.

| PORTFOLIO ACTIVITY SUMMARY | | | | |
|---|---|---|---|---|
| Criteria | Portfolio page reference | 0–1 | 1–4 | 4–7 |
| C.2.5.c&f | See page 29 for Portfolio Activity | | | |
| C.2.5.d | See page 29 for Portfolio Activity | | | |

C.2.5.a    Describe how exercise can promote the physical growth and development of a 1–4 year old and a 4–7 year old child.

..................................................................................................................................................

..................................................................................................................................................

..................................................................................................................................................

..................................................................................................................................................

..................................................................................................................................................

..................................................................................................................................................

C.2.5.b    Why is it important to supervise children during physical exercise?

..................................................................................................................................................

..................................................................................................................................................

..................................................................................................................................................

..................................................................................................................................................

..................................................................................................................................................

### C.2.5.c&f Portfolio Activity

*Plan and implement ONE activity which will promote the physical development of a child. Explain why you chose the activity and what the child gained from it.*

### C.2.5.d Portfolio Activity

*Describe how the work setting makes changes to the equipment and space to meet the children's physical needs while ensuring safety.*

C.2.5.e    'Boys play football and girls play with skipping ropes'.
Describe how the child care and education worker can promote non-stereotypical exercise and play.

..................................................................................................................................................

..................................................................................................................................................

........................................................................................................

........................................................................................................

C.2.5.g    Describe how a child's self-confidence can be developed through physical exercise.

........................................................................................................

........................................................................................................

........................................................................................................

........................................................................................................

# C.4 SUPPORT CHILDREN'S SOCIAL AND EMOTIONAL DEVELOPMENT
## UNIT WIDE KNOWLEDGE

| Criteria | Knowledge evidence | Date completed |
|----------|-------------------|----------------|
| C.4.a | Basic knowledge of children's social and emotional development 6 weeks to 8 years and how this relates to other aspects of their development. | |
| C.4.b | Observation of children and use of the information gained to evaluate children's social and emotional development. | |
| C.4.c | The needs of children with respect to social and emotional development and how these needs may be met. | |
| C.4.d | How a child's previous early experiences affect his/her individual needs and can shape early attitudes and behaviour. | |
| C.4.e | Social and environmental factors which could have an adverse effect on children's emotional development. | |
| C.4.f | How children under stress can regress socially and emotionally. | |
| C.4.g | How stereotypical views in carers can hinder the growth of children's independence and their emotional and social development. | |
| C.4.h | A range of activities and intervention strategies which support and encourage social and emotional development in children. | |

| C.4.i | The role of play and its potential as an aid to social and emotional development. | |
|---|---|---|
| C.4.j | The effects on children's social and emotional development of lack of play opportunities. | |
| C.4.k | Recognition of racist, sexist, abusive and anti-social behaviour. | |
| C.4.l | How to challenge racist, sexist, abusive and anti-social behaviour. | |
| C.4.m | The need to offer comfort and support wherever appropriate. | |
| C.4.n | How a child's special needs will affect their social and emotional development. | |
| C.4.o | The particular difficulties which may affect the social and emotional development of children who use more than one language. | |
| C.4.p | Assessment of materials and equipment which help towards the social and emotional development of children. | |
| C.4.q | Relationships with a range of adults and children outside the family are important for children's social and emotional development. | |
| C.4.r | The importance of valuing and respecting the child as an individual and the role of the professional worker in encouraging this in other children and adults including parents. | |

## USEFUL BOOKS

*Special Issues in Child Care.* M. O'Hagan and M. Smith (1993) Bailliere Tindall.
*Caring for the under 8s.* Jennie and Lance Lindon (1993) Macmillan.
*The Developing Child.* 5th ed. Helen Bee (1989) Harper Collins.
*Self-Esteem and Successful Early Learning.* Rosemary Roberts (1995) Hodder and Stoughton.

## PORTFOLIO ACTIVITY SUMMARY

| Criteria | Portfolio page reference | 0–1 | 1–4 | 4–7 |
|----------|--------------------------|-----|-----|-----|
| C.4.a | See page 34 for Portfolio Activity | | | |
| C.4.b | See page 34 for Portfolio Activity | | | |
| C.4.h | See pages 35–6 for Portfolio Activity | | | |

# C.4 Support children's social and emotional development

### C.4.a Portfolio Activity

*Design a booklet for parents which explains the development of a young child from 6 weeks to 8 years. The booklet should highlight the significant stages of social and emotional development.*

### C.4.b Portfolio Activity

*Observe the emotional and social development of children of different ages. Explain the importance of observing children and how you can use the information to encourage the emotional and social development of the child.*

C.4.c    Name TWO emotional needs that a child may have. Describe how the child care and education worker can meet these needs.

........................................................................................................................

........................................................................................................................

........................................................................................................................

........................................................................................................................

Name TWO social needs that a child may have. Describe how the child care and education worker can meet these needs.

........................................................................................................................

........................................................................................................................

........................................................................................................................

........................................................................................................................

C.4.d    Describe how a child's early experiences can positively AND negatively affect his/her social and emotional development.

........................................................................................................................

........................................................................................................................

..............................................................................................................

..............................................................................................................

C.4.e    Name TWO social factors that could have an adverse effect on the social and emotional development of a child.

..............................................................................................................

..............................................................................................................

Name TWO environmental factors that could have an adverse effect on the social and emotional development of a child.

..............................................................................................................

..............................................................................................................

C.4.f    Briefly describe TWO situations which may cause stress for a child. For each situation, explain how the behaviour of the child may be affected.

..............................................................................................................

..............................................................................................................

..............................................................................................................

..............................................................................................................

C.4.g    'Big boys don't cry'.
What effect can this type of statement have on a child's emotional development?

..............................................................................................................

..............................................................................................................

..............................................................................................................

..............................................................................................................

## C.4.h Portfolio Activity

*Plan and implement THREE different activities which can support and encourage a child's social and emotional development. Explain how effective each activity was.*

### C.4.h Portfolio Activity

*Observe the social activities of a child at regular intervals throughout the day. Explain the role of the adult in supporting and encouraging the social and emotional development of the child.*

C.4.i    How can play encourage a child's social and emotional development?

.........................................................................................................................................

.........................................................................................................................................

.........................................................................................................................................

.........................................................................................................................................

.........................................................................................................................................

.........................................................................................................................................

C.4.j    What effect can a lack of play activities have on a child's emotional and social development?

.........................................................................................................................................

.........................................................................................................................................

.........................................................................................................................................

.........................................................................................................................................

.........................................................................................................................................

.........................................................................................................................................

C.4.k&l    How can the following types of behaviour affect a child's social and emotional behaviour? For EACH type of behaviour suggest ways in which the carer can promote positive attitudes.

(*a*) racist behaviour;

.........................................................................................................................................

.........................................................................................................................................

.........................................................................................................................................

(*b*) sexist behaviour;

..................................................................................................

..................................................................................................

..................................................................................................

(*c*) abusive behaviour;

..................................................................................................

..................................................................................................

..................................................................................................

(*d*) anti-social behaviour.

..................................................................................................

..................................................................................................

..................................................................................................

C.4.m    Why is it important to give comfort and support to a child?

..................................................................................................

..................................................................................................

..................................................................................................

..................................................................................................

C.4.n    How may a child's special needs affect his/her social and emotional development?

..................................................................................................

..................................................................................................

..................................................................................................

..................................................................................................

C.4.o    What emotional and social difficulties could a bilingual child have?

..................................................................................................................

..................................................................................................................

..................................................................................................................

..................................................................................................................

C.4.p    Complete the table below. THREE pieces of equipment and/or materials have been given to you. You will need to add THREE more pieces of equipment or materials.

| Equipment/materials | Effectiveness of equipment/materials in promoting social and emotional development |
|---|---|
| Dolls<br><br>Water<br><br>Clay | |

C.4.q    Why is it important for children to meet adults who are not part of the family?

..................................................................................................................

..................................................................................................................

..................................................................................................................

..................................................................................................................

C.4.r    Why is it important for the child care and education worker to respect and value each child as an individual?

..................................................................................................................

..................................................................................................................

..................................................................................................................

..................................................................................................................

How can the child care and education worker encourage other adults to respect and value the child?

..................................................................................................................

..................................................................................................................

..................................................................................................................

..................................................................................................................

# C.4.1 Help children to relate to others

<table>
<tr><td rowspan="4" style="vertical-align:middle">PROGRESS CHECKLIST</td><td>Criteria</td><td>Knowledge evidence</td><td>Date completed</td></tr>
<tr><td>C.4.1.a</td><td>The individual needs, with regard to social and emotional development, of the children in the setting, and ways of meeting these needs.</td><td></td></tr>
<tr><td>C.4.1.b</td><td>The role of the adult in the resolution of conflict situations among children and the rationale behind it.</td><td></td></tr>
<tr><td>C.4.1.c</td><td>The importance of adults as role models.</td><td></td></tr>
</table>

## USEFUL BOOKS

*Caring for the under 8s.* Jennie and Lance Lindon (1993) Macmillan.

| PORTFOLIO ACTIVITY SUMMARY | | | | |
|---|---|---|---|---|
| **Criteria** | **Portfolio page reference** | **0–1** | **1–4** | **4–7** |
| C.4.1.a | See below for Portfolio Activity | | | |

 ### C.4.1.a Portfolio Activity

*Observe on ONE occasion the child/children's emotional and social needs in the work setting. Explain how the child care and education worker may meet the needs of the child/children.*

C.4.1.b    Describe how the child care and education worker can encourage a child to cooperate and respect:

(*a*) other children;
(*b*) adults.

Give reasons for your action.

........................................................................................................................................

........................................................................................................................................

..........................................................................................................

..........................................................................................................

..........................................................................................................

..........................................................................................................

..........................................................................................................

..........................................................................................................

..........................................................................................................

..........................................................................................................

..........................................................................................................

C.4.1.c    Why is it important for the adult to provide a good role model to the child?

..........................................................................................................

..........................................................................................................

..........................................................................................................

..........................................................................................................

..........................................................................................................

..........................................................................................................

## C.4.2 Help children to develop self-reliance and self-esteem

| | Criteria | Knowledge evidence | Date completed |
|---|---|---|---|
| **PROGRESS CHECKLIST** | C.4.2.a | A range of activities, routines and strategies which encourage respect for the individual child and understand the rationale behind these. | |
| | C.4.2.b | The importance of self-respect among adult workers and of knowledge of self. | |
| | C.4.2.c | The development of self-reliance and self-esteem as a gradual process and how this is affected by maturation and the development of communication skills in the child. | |
| | C.4.2.d | The importance of communication with and knowing how to listen to and encourage interaction between children as adults and children. | |
| | C.4.2.e | When it is appropriate to give responsibility to children, why this is important and that family/cultural expectations of this may vary and should be handled sensitively. | |
| | C.4.2.f | When to praise a child for his/her efforts and the rationale behind positive reinforcement for effort. | |
| | C.4.2.g | A range of strategies to encourage negotiation with children, know their possible outcomes and understand the need for flexibility in their application. | |
| | C.4.2.h | How to provide activities and strategies to promote self-reliance and self-esteem and how they may be adjusted to take account of children from different cultural backgrounds, genders and with special needs. | |
| | C.4.2.i | How to interact with parents in a manner which reinforces the self-image of the child and the adult and supports positive interaction between parents and child. | |

## USEFUL BOOKS

*Self-Esteem and Successful Early Learning.* Rosemary Roberts (1995) Hodder and Stoughton.
*Learning to be Strong.* Margy Whalley (1994) Hodder and Stoughton.

| PORTFOLIO ACTIVITY SUMMARY | | 0–1 | 1–4 | 4–7 |
|---|---|---|---|---|
| **Criteria** | **Portfolio page reference** | | | |
| C.4.2.a | See below for Portfolio Activity | | | |
| C.4.2.d | See page 44 for Portfolio Activity | | | |
| C.4.2.g | See page 45 for Portfolio Activity | | | |
| C.4.2.h | See page 45 for Portfolio Activity | | | |

 ### *C.4.2.a Portfolio Activity*

*Plan and implement activities which will encourage the self-respect of a child. Give reasons for your choice of activity.*

C.4.2.b    Why is it important for an adult to have self-respect when working with young children?

..............................................................................................................................

..............................................................................................................................

..............................................................................................................................

..............................................................................................................................

C.4.2.c    Describe the way in which a child develops self-reliance and self-esteem. Explain how it is affected by maturation and the development of communication skills.

..............................................................................................................................

..............................................................................................................................

..................................................................................................................

..................................................................................................................

..................................................................................................................

..................................................................................................................

..................................................................................................................

..................................................................................................................

..................................................................................................................

## C.4.2.d Portfolio Activity

*Observe an adult encouraging a child by either talking to or listening to the child. Explain how effective the interaction was.*

C.4.2.e   Why is it appropriate to give responsibility to children and when is it appropriate to do so? Remember to take family and cultural expectations into account.

..................................................................................................................

..................................................................................................................

..................................................................................................................

..................................................................................................................

..................................................................................................................

..................................................................................................................

C.4.2.f   What is meant by positive reinforcement and why should a child care and education worker use positive reinforcement when working with a child?

..................................................................................................................

..................................................................................................................

..........................................................................................................

..........................................................................................................

..........................................................................................................

..........................................................................................................

 ## C.4.2.g Portfolio Activity

*Describe situations where you have negotiated with a child in order to:*

      (*a*) *achieve a task; and*

    ..........................................................................................................

    ..........................................................................................................

    (*b*) *resolve a dilemma.*

    ..........................................................................................................

    ..........................................................................................................

 ## C.4.2.h Portfolio Activity

*Plan and implement ONE activity which encourages self-reliance and self-esteem. Account should be taken of the child's cultural background, gender and any special needs. Explain how effective the activities have been in meeting the needs of the child.*

C.4.2.i    Explain how the child care and education worker can interact with the parent in a manner which encourages the self-image of the child and the adult.

..........................................................................................................

..........................................................................................................

..........................................................................................................

..........................................................................................................

..........................................................................................................

..........................................................................................................

# C.4.3 Help children to recognise and deal with their feelings

| | Criteria | Knowledge evidence | Date completed |
|---|---|---|---|
| **PROGRESS CHECKLIST** | C.4.3.a | Social and environmental factors which affect children and families. | |
| | C.4.3.b | The wide range of emotions, both positive and negative, covered by the term 'feelings'. | |
| | C.4.3.c | The importance for the child's social and emotional development of learning to recognise, name and deal with their feelings and the feelings of others. | |
| | C.4.3.d | The powerful nature of feelings in young children and what expectations of control would be appropriate. | |
| | C.4.3.e | Strategies for encouraging the expression of positive and negative feelings in words and actions where appropriate. | |
| | C.4.3.f | Expression of feeling should not be governed by cultural or gender stereotyping. | |
| | C.4.3.g | Recognition of signs of distress in a child. | |
| | C.4.3.h | Recognition of emotional outbursts and negative reactions and appropriate strategies which lead to positive outcomes. | |
| | C.4.3.i | The rationale behind a calm and reassuring manner when dealing with children who are emotionally upset, including awareness of safety and minimum disruption to other children. | |
| | C.4.3.j | Learning opportunities which arise in the daily routine to help children to express, discuss and control their feelings, and strategies for maximising the potential of these opportunities to help children develop socially and emotionally. | |
| | C.4.3.k | The role of the carer and boundaries of confidentiality with regard to the sharing of concern about children's emotional and social development with parents, colleagues and other professionals. | |

## USEFUL BOOKS

*Caring for Young Children.* Jennie and Lance Lindon (1994) Macmillan.

| PORTFOLIO ACTIVITY SUMMARY | | 0–1 | 1–4 | 4–7 |
|---|---|---|---|---|
| **Criteria** | **Portfolio page reference** | | | |
| C.4.3.h | See page 48 for Portfolio Activity | | | |
| C.4.3.j | See page 49 for Portfolio Activity | | | |

C.4.3.a    Name TWO social and TWO environmental factors which affect the emotions of children and their families.

........................................................................................................

........................................................................................................

........................................................................................................

........................................................................................................

C.4.3.b    Name THREE positive and THREE negative emotions.

........................................................................................................

........................................................................................................

........................................................................................................

C.4.3.c    Why is it important for a child to learn to recognise and deal with his/her feelings?

........................................................................................................

........................................................................................................

........................................................................................................

........................................................................................................

C.4.3.d   A 2-year-old child is having a temper tantrum in a shop. Is this unusual behaviour for a child? Give reasons for your answer.

..............................................................................................................................

..............................................................................................................................

..............................................................................................................................

..............................................................................................................................

A 7-year-old child is having a temper tantrum at school. Is this unusual behaviour for a child? Give reasons for your answer.

..............................................................................................................................

..............................................................................................................................

..............................................................................................................................

..............................................................................................................................

C.4.3.e&f   Describe how the child care and education worker can encourage a child to show his/her positive AND negative feelings, regardless of gender.

..............................................................................................................................

..............................................................................................................................

..............................................................................................................................

..............................................................................................................................

C.4.3.g   Name THREE signs of distress in a child other than crying.

..............................................................................................................................

..............................................................................................................................

..............................................................................................................................

## C.4.3.h Portfolio Activity

*Observe a child who is distressed and being comforted by an adult. Describe how the child care and education worker calmed the child.*

C.4.3.i    Why is it important for the child care and education worker to have a quiet and calm manner when working with a distressed child?

..............................................................................................................................

..............................................................................................................................

..............................................................................................................................

..............................................................................................................................

## C.4.3.j Portfolio Activity

*Plan and implement ONE activity which would allow a child to express his/her feelings. In the evaluation, describe how effective you think the activity was.*

C.4.3.k    Describe the role of the child care and education worker in maintaining confidentiality when discussing a child's emotional and social development with the parent or other staff.

..............................................................................................................................

..............................................................................................................................

..............................................................................................................................

..............................................................................................................................

# C.4.4 Prepare children for moving on to new settings

<table>
<tr><td rowspan="9" style="writing-mode:vertical-lr">PROGRESS CHECKLIST</td><td>**Criteria**</td><td>**Knowledge evidence**</td><td>**Date completed**</td></tr>
<tr><td>C.4.4.a</td><td>Children's needs with regard to change and the importance of preparing for and managing transitions.</td><td></td></tr>
<tr><td>C.4.4.b</td><td>Knowledge of child care/education provision available.</td><td></td></tr>
<tr><td>C.4.4.c</td><td>The effects of separation and how this can affect young children.</td><td></td></tr>
<tr><td>C.4.4.d</td><td>The carer's own role and that of others involved in arrangements and what action is appropriate to minimise stress in transitions.</td><td></td></tr>
<tr><td>C.4.4.e</td><td>The levels of understanding of the child and the importance of giving them information according to this level.</td><td></td></tr>
<tr><td>C.4.4.f</td><td>The importance of parental involvement in decision making.</td><td></td></tr>
<tr><td>C.4.4.g</td><td>Appropriate play activities to encourage positive expectations of the new setting and role of the carer in these activities.</td><td></td></tr>
<tr><td>C.4.4.h</td><td>The importance of recognising and making use of opportunities to familiarise children with new settings.</td><td></td></tr>
</table>

## USEFUL BOOKS

*Special Issues in Child Care.* M. O'Hagan and M. Smith (1993) Bailliere Tindall.

| PORTFOLIO ACTIVITY SUMMARY | | 0–1 | 1–4 | 4–7 |
|---|---|---|---|---|
| **Criteria** | **Portfolio page reference** | | | |
| C.4.4.b | See below for Portfolio Activity | | | |
| C.4.4.g&h | See page 53 for Portfolio Activity | | | |

C.4.4.a    Describe the needs of a child when moving to new settings.

.................................................................................................................

.................................................................................................................

.................................................................................................................

.................................................................................................................

.................................................................................................................

.................................................................................................................

Why is it important to prepare the child for the change?

.................................................................................................................

.................................................................................................................

.................................................................................................................

.................................................................................................................

.................................................................................................................

.................................................................................................................

### C.4.4.b Portfolio Activity

*Design a booklet for parents which explains the provision that is available for the 1–4 year old AND the 4–7 years 11 months old child in the local area. Give FIVE examples for EACH age group.*

C.4.4.c    When moving to a new setting, what effect can the separation from the parent have on the child?

........................................................................................................

........................................................................................................

........................................................................................................

........................................................................................................

........................................................................................................

........................................................................................................

C.4.4.d    Describe the role of the child care and education worker in helping a child cope with moving to a new setting. What can he/she do to make it as stress-free as possible?

........................................................................................................

........................................................................................................

........................................................................................................

........................................................................................................

........................................................................................................

........................................................................................................

C.4.4.e    Why is it important to take the child's level of understanding into account when telling them about a move to a new setting?

........................................................................................................

........................................................................................................

........................................................................................................

........................................................................................................

C.4.4.f    Why is it important to involve the parent in decision making?

........................................................................................................

......................................................................................................

......................................................................................................

......................................................................................................

### C.4.4.g&h Portfolio Activity

*Plan and implement an activity that will help to prepare a child for a new setting.*

# C.4.5 Help children to adjust to the care/education setting

| | Criteria | Knowledge evidence | Date completed |
|---|---|---|---|
| **PROGRESS CHECKLIST** | C.4.5.a | Awareness of young children's needs in relation to change and separation and that these may vary with individuals. | |
| | C.4.5.b | The effects of change and the importance of sympathetic and appropriate handling including physical contact. | |
| | C.4.5.c | Sensitivity to the role played by transitional objects and activities as agreed with parents. | |
| | C.4.5.d | The importance of, and method of, welcoming children and recognising their individual needs. | |
| | C.4.5.e | The importance of a familiarisation programme which takes into consideration both the level of development of the child and his/her emotional state. | |
| | C.4.5.f | The rationale behind the strategies of the care/education setting for settling in children and the need for flexibility. | |
| | C.4.5.g | How children differ in the time taken to adjust to the care/education setting and the different types and levels of support required. | |
| | C.4.5.h | The importance of preparing children and adults in the new setting to receive newcomers. | |
| | C.4.5.i | How to impart information to parents in a manner which does not raise anxiety but nevertheless alerts them to potential or actual causes for concern. | |

# USEFUL BOOKS

*Special Issues in Child Care.* M. O'Hagan and M. Smith (1993) Balliere Tindall.

| PORTFOLIO ACTIVITY SUMMARY | | | | |
|---|---|---|---|---|
| **Criteria** | **Portfolio page reference** | **0–1** | **1–4** | **4–7** |
| C.4.5.d | See page 56 for Portfolio Activity | | | |
| C.4.5.e&f | See page 56 for Portfolio Activity | | | |

C.4.5.a    Describe the needs of a child who has started in a new setting.

..................................................................................................................

..................................................................................................................

..................................................................................................................

..................................................................................................................

C.4.5.b    Why is it important for the child care and education worker to work with the new child in a sensitive way?

..................................................................................................................

..................................................................................................................

..................................................................................................................

..................................................................................................................

C.4.5.c    Why is it important for the child care and education worker to be sensitive to the child's use of toys or materials as comforters?

..................................................................................................................

..................................................................................................................

..................................................................................................................

..................................................................................................................

### C.4.5.d Portfolio Activity

*Describe how you would welcome the child/children to the work setting at the start of a day. Explain why it is important to do this.*

### C.4.5.e&f Portfolio Activity

*Design a programme which may be used to help a child AND the parent become familiar with a new setting. Give reasons for content of the programme and explain the value of it.*

C.4.5.g　Why do some children take longer to settle into a new situation than others?

.......................................................................................................................

.......................................................................................................................

.......................................................................................................................

.......................................................................................................................

C.4.5.h　Why is it important to tell the children and staff in the work setting that a new child is starting?

.......................................................................................................................

.......................................................................................................................

.......................................................................................................................

.......................................................................................................................

C.4.5.i　How can the child care and education worker give information to the parent without causing anxiety?

.......................................................................................................................

.......................................................................................................................

.......................................................................................................................

.......................................................................................................................

# C.6 CONTRIBUTE TO THE MANAGEMENT OF CHILDREN'S BEHAVIOUR
## UNIT WIDE KNOWLEDGE

| | Criteria | Knowledge evidence | Date completed |
|---|---|---|---|
| **PROGRESS CHECKLIST** | C.6.a | Ways in which the candidate can contribute positively and negatively to children's behaviour. | |
| | C.6.b | Basic knowledge of children's development 6 weeks to 8 years and how this affects their behaviour. | |
| | C.6.c | Key indicators of development and problem behaviour. Emotional, physical, intellectual, social, language. | |
| | C.6.d | Understand that there could be a variety of possible reasons for delayed and regressive behaviour. | |
| | C.6.e | The importance of the causes and antecedents of behaviour, learned or environmental. | |
| | C.6.f | Norms and expectations of behaviour as influences by class, culture, religion, race, age, in both simple/complex behaviours. | |
| | C.6.g | Methods and techniques for verbal and non-verbal communication with adults and children and reasons for use. | |
| | C.6.h | Own role in the setting, the roles of other workers and the liaison between other professional groups. | |

## USEFUL BOOKS

*Caring for the under 8s.* Jennie and Lance Lindon (1993) Macmillan.
*Special Issues in Child Care.* M. O'Hagan and M. Smith (1993) Bailliere Tindall.
*Behaviour Problems in Young Children.* Jo Douglas (1989) Tavistock/Routledge.
*Working with Young Children (Part three).* Jennie Laishley (1987) Hodder and Stoughton.

| PORTFOLIO ACTIVITY SUMMARY | | | | |
|---|---|---|---|---|
| Criteria | Portfolio page reference | 0–1 | 1–4 | 4–7 |
| C.6.b | See page 59 for Portfolio Activity | | | |
| C.6.c | See page 59 for Portfolio Activity | | | |

# C.6 Contribute to the management of children's behaviour

C.6.a    Describe how the child care and education worker can encourage positive behaviour in children.

......................................................................................................................................................

......................................................................................................................................................

......................................................................................................................................................

......................................................................................................................................................

......................................................................................................................................................

Describe how the child care and education worker can promote negative behaviour in children.

......................................................................................................................................................

......................................................................................................................................................

......................................................................................................................................................

......................................................................................................................................................

......................................................................................................................................................

 ### C.6.b Portfolio Activity

*Design a booklet for parents which explains the development of a child from 6 weeks to 8 years. Explain how the development of the child can affect his/her behaviour.*

 ### C.6.c Portfolio Activity

*Observe THREE children of different ages on SEPARATE occasions. Describe their behaviour in relation to their stage of development.*

C.6.d    What could cause delayed behaviour? Give TWO reasons.

......................................................................................................................................................

......................................................................................................................................................

What could cause a child's behaviour to regress? Give TWO reasons.

..............................................................................................................

..............................................................................................................

C.6.e    Why is it important for the child care and education worker to understand what caused the behaviour of the child?

..............................................................................................................

..............................................................................................................

C.6.f    Behaviour is often influenced by race, class, culture, religion or age. Give THREE examples of comments you have heard adults make when talking about a particular child's behaviour.

..............................................................................................................

..............................................................................................................

..............................................................................................................

C.6.g    Describe how an adult can communicate with a young child by means of

(*a*) verbal communication;

..............................................................................................................

..............................................................................................................

..............................................................................................................

..............................................................................................................

(*b*) non-verbal communication.

..............................................................................................................

..............................................................................................................

..............................................................................................................

..............................................................................................................

(**NB** *You may have answered this in C.2.f.*)

# C.6.1 Contribute to a framework for children's behaviour

| | Criteria | Knowledge evidence | Date completed |
|---|---|---|---|
| **PROGRESS CHECKLIST** | C.6.1.a | The limitations of children's memory and understanding and how this may affect their ability to comply with goals and boundaries for behaviour. | |
| | C.6.1.b | The reasons why frameworks for children's behaviour are necessary. | |

## USEFUL BOOKS

*An Introduction to Child Developments.* G. C. Davenport (1994) Collins.
*Special Issues in Child Care.* M. O'Hagan and M. Smith (1993) Bailliere Tindall.

C.6.1.a    The child care and education worker found a 2-year-old child playing with the television although he/she had been told the previous week that it was dangerous and should not be played with. Is this behaviour unusual for a child of this age? Give reasons for your answer.

.......................................................................................................................

.......................................................................................................................

.......................................................................................................................

.......................................................................................................................

.......................................................................................................................

.......................................................................................................................

C.6.1.b    Why is it important to give children goals and boundaries with regard to behaviour?

.......................................................................................................................

.......................................................................................................................

.......................................................................................................................

.......................................................................................................................

.......................................................................................................................

# C.6.2 Promote positive aspects of children's behaviour

| | Criteria | Knowledge evidence | Date completed |
|---|---|---|---|
| PROGRESS CHECKLIST | C.6.2.a | The concept of socially acceptable/desirable behaviour and how this may vary across settings and cultures. | |
| | C.6.2.b | The basic principles of behaviour modification and why it is important actively to promote positive aspects of behaviour. | |
| | C.6.2.c | The rationale behind offering explanations and discussion of socially desirable behaviour to children. | |

## USEFUL BOOKS

*Caring for the Under 8s.* Jennie and Lance Lindon (1993) Macmillan.
*Special Issues in Child Care.* M. O'Hagan and M. Smith (1993) Bailliere Tindall.

C.6.2.a    Describe what is meant by 'socially acceptable behaviour'?

.......................................................................................................................................

.......................................................................................................................................

.......................................................................................................................................

.......................................................................................................................................

C.6.2.b    Describe TWO ways in which the child care and education worker could help a child to develop socially acceptable behaviour. Your answer should include why it is important to encourage positive behaviour.

.......................................................................................................................................

.......................................................................................................................................

.......................................................................................................................................

.......................................................................................................................................

C.6.2.c    Why is it valuable to explain to a child that what he/she has done is not acceptable?

..........................................................................................................................................

..........................................................................................................................................

..........................................................................................................................................

..........................................................................................................................................

# C.6.3 *Manage unwanted aspects of children's behaviour*

| Criteria | Knowledge evidence | Date completed |
|---|---|---|
| C.6.3.a | The factors and circumstances which may encourage or provoke children to display difficult or negative behaviour. | |
| C.6.3.b | The reasons why a calm and controlled manner is important and why physical punishment is not necessary, acceptable or effective. | |
| C.6.3.c | The basic principles of behaviour modification and how they can be used to manage children's unwanted behaviour. | |
| C.6.3.d | The importance of boundary setting and consistency of application by significant adults. | |
| C.6.3.e | Principles for selecting reward system to be used when dealing with problem behaviour. | |
| C.6.3.f | Techniques of physical and non-physical control. | |
| C.6.3.g | Legal implications of physical and/or other methods of control. | |

## USEFUL BOOKS

*Caring for the under 8s.* Jennie and Lance Lindon (1993) Macmillan.
*Special Issues in Child Care.* M. O'Hagan and M. Smith (1993) Bailliere Tindall.

C.6.3.a    List THREE factors and/or circumstances which may encourage a child to behave in an unacceptable way.

.........................................................................................................................................

.........................................................................................................................................

.........................................................................................................................................

C.6.3.b   Why should the child care and education worker remain calm when helping a child whose behaviour is giving cause for concern?

..........................................................................................................................

..........................................................................................................................

..........................................................................................................................

..........................................................................................................................

C.6.3.c   A 4-year-old child is biting other children and adults in the work setting. Describe how the child care and education worker could help the child understand that this behaviour is not acceptable.

..........................................................................................................................

..........................................................................................................................

..........................................................................................................................

..........................................................................................................................

C.6.3.d   Why is it important for adults to use the same rules of behaviour when working with children?

..........................................................................................................................

..........................................................................................................................

..........................................................................................................................

..........................................................................................................................

C.6.3.e   List TWO reward systems which could be used to encourage socially acceptable behaviour in children. Explain how the child care and education worker can decide which is the best method to use.

..........................................................................................................................

..........................................................................................................................

..........................................................................................................................

..........................................................................................................................

C.6.3.f    Describe ONE method of physical control and ONE method of non-physical control which could be used by the child care and education worker.

..............................................................................................................................

..............................................................................................................................

..............................................................................................................................

..............................................................................................................................

C.6.3.g    Describe the possible implications for a child care and education worker who uses physical control as a method of controlling children.

..............................................................................................................................

..............................................................................................................................

..............................................................................................................................

..............................................................................................................................

# C.8 Set out and clear away play activities
## Unit wide knowledge

| | Criteria | Knowledge evidence | Date completed |
|---|---|---|---|
| PROGRESS CHECKLIST | C.8.a | The purpose and potential of play activities for children at different levels of development. | |
| | C.8.b | The role of play in children's development. | |
| | C.8.c | Health and safety requirements of the setting. | |
| | C.8.d | The role of an overall curriculum plan in relation to selection, layout and presentation of materials and equipment for children's activities. | |

## Useful books

*A Practical Guide to Activities with Young Children.* Jill Frankel and Christine Hobart (1994) Stanley Thornes.
*Special Issues in Child Care.* M. O'Hagan and M. Smith (1993) Bailliere Tindall.

There are many other books available on this topic. It is important to visit the library or local book shop to look at the wide range available.

# C.8 Set out and clear away play activities

C.8.a     Fill in the table below. (**NB** *It may be easier to complete this table AFTER you have worked through the unit.*)

| Types of play | Purpose of play activities | Potential of play activities |
|---|---|---|
| Creative Play 1–4 years | | |
| Creative Play 4–7.11 years | | |
| Role play 1–4 years | | |
| Role play 4–7.11 years | | |
| Manipulative play 1–4 years | | |
| Manipulative play 4–7.11 years | | |
| Physical play 1–4 years | | |
| Physical play 4–7.11 years | | |

You may wish to copy and complete this table and enter it in your portfolio.

C.8.b     'My child always seems to be playing and never works'.
Describe the value of play as part of a child's development.

........................................................................................................................

........................................................................................................................

........................................................................................................................

..............................................................................................................................

..............................................................................................................................

..............................................................................................................................

..............................................................................................................................

..............................................................................................................................

..............................................................................................................................

..............................................................................................................................

..............................................................................................................................

**C.8.c**  Describe the health and safety requirements of the work setting in relation to play materials.

..............................................................................................................................

..............................................................................................................................

..............................................................................................................................

..............................................................................................................................

..............................................................................................................................

..............................................................................................................................

**C.8.d**  Why is it important to have an overall curriculum plan when deciding on the selection, layout and presentation of materials and equipment for children's activities? (**NB** *Consider unexpected situations beyond your control.*)

..............................................................................................................................

..............................................................................................................................

..............................................................................................................................

..............................................................................................................................

..............................................................................................................................

# *C.8.1.a Set out natural and other materials for creative play*

<table>
<tr><th></th><th>Criteria</th><th>Knowledge evidence</th><th>Date completed</th></tr>
<tr><td rowspan="10">PROGRESS CHECKLIST</td><td>C.8.1.a</td><td>What creative play is and how it assists learning and development.</td><td></td></tr>
<tr><td>C.8.1.b</td><td>The kinds of materials involved in creative play and their properties.</td><td></td></tr>
<tr><td>C.8.1.c</td><td>The potential hazards and the safety measures associated with natural and other materials.</td><td></td></tr>
<tr><td>C.8.1.d</td><td>Which materials are natural and which are 'other' materials.</td><td></td></tr>
<tr><td>C.8.1.e</td><td>A range of ways to set out and present materials attractively.</td><td></td></tr>
</table>

## USEFUL BOOKS

*Special Issues in Child Care.* M. O'Hagan and M. Smith (1993) Bailliere Tindall.

## PORTFOLIO ACTIVITY SUMMARY

| Criteria | Portfolio page reference | 0–1 | 1–4 | 4–7 |
|---|---|---|---|---|
| C.8.1.e | See page 71 for Portfolio Activity | | | |

C.8.1.a    What is 'creative play'?

.............................................................................................................

.............................................................................................................

.............................................................................................................

Describe how creative play can help children's development?

..................................................................................................................

..................................................................................................................

..................................................................................................................

..................................................................................................................

C.8.1.b    Name FIVE materials which could be provided to promote creative play.

..................................................................................................................

..................................................................................................................

..................................................................................................................

..................................................................................................................

..................................................................................................................

C.8.1.c    What safety considerations must be taken into account when working with natural and other materials?

..................................................................................................................

..................................................................................................................

..................................................................................................................

..................................................................................................................

C.8.1.d    Name THREE 'natural' materials and THREE 'other' materials.

..................................................................................................................

..................................................................................................................

..................................................................................................................

 ### C.8.1.e Portfolio Activity
*Plan and implement different ways of setting out natural and other materials.*

# C.8.2 Set up physical play activities with large equipment

| Criteria | Knowledge evidence | Date completed |
|----------|-------------------|----------------|
| C.8.2.a | Potential uses of equipment and ways of modifying equipment for children with special needs. | |
| C.8.2.b | The importance of children having opportunities for outdoor play. | |
| C.8.2.c | The types and uses of equipment in relation to physical activities and development. | |
| C.8.2.d | The various purposes of each piece of equipment. | |
| C.8.2.e | How to use space effectively and safely. | |
| C.8.2.f | The appropriate uses of equipment in relation to ages and sequence of development. | |
| C.8.2.g | The need to present a challenge through the equipment, when to challenge and when to consolidate learning. | |
| C.8.2.h | How to set up equipment safely and potential risks to safety, including ways of preventing accidents. | |

## USEFUL BOOKS

The unit wide knowledge books will help you with this section.

## PORTFOLIO ACTIVITY SUMMARY

| Criteria | Portfolio page reference | 0–1 | 1–4 | 4–7 |
|----------|-------------------------|-----|-----|-----|
| C.8.2.e | See page 74 for Portfolio Activity | | | |

C.8.2.a,c    Give THREE different examples of equipment that may be used for EACH of
d&f          the headings given below.

(*a*) Climbing equipment

..............................................................................................................................................................

..............................................................................................................................................................

..............................................................................................................................................................

(*b*) Equipment for climbing through

..............................................................................................................................................................

..............................................................................................................................................................

..............................................................................................................................................................

(*c*) Equipment for sliding or bouncing on

..............................................................................................................................................................

..............................................................................................................................................................

..............................................................................................................................................................

(*d*) Moving equipment

..............................................................................................................................................................

..............................................................................................................................................................

..............................................................................................................................................................

Select ONE piece of equipment for EACH of the headings in C.8.2.a and
explain how the equipment may be used with children of different age groups
i.e. 1–4 and 4–7 years 11 months.

..............................................................................................................................................................

..............................................................................................................................................................

..............................................................................................................................................................

..............................................................................................................................................................

..............................................................................................................

..............................................................................................................

Select ONE piece of equipment from C.8.2.a and explain how the equipment may be adapted for children with a disability.

..............................................................................................................

..............................................................................................................

..............................................................................................................

..............................................................................................................

C.8.2.b    Why is it important for children to have the opportunity to play outside?

..............................................................................................................

..............................................................................................................

..............................................................................................................

..............................................................................................................

..............................................................................................................

 ### C.8.2.e Portfolio Activity

*Describe how the work setting uses its space effectively and safely.*

C.8.2.g    Why is it important to set challenges for the children through the use of equipment?

..............................................................................................................

..............................................................................................................

..............................................................................................................

..............................................................................................................

How can the child care and education worker consolidate a child's learning?

...................................................................................................................

...................................................................................................................

...................................................................................................................

...................................................................................................................

...................................................................................................................

...................................................................................................................

C.8.2.h    List THREE safety factors that should be taken into account for EACH of the
following types of equipment:

(*a*) sliding and bouncing equipment;

...................................................................................................................

...................................................................................................................

...................................................................................................................

(*b*) climbing equipment.

...................................................................................................................

...................................................................................................................

...................................................................................................................

# C.8.3 Provide opportunities and materials to stimulate role play

<table>
<tr><td rowspan="7" style="writing-mode: vertical-lr">PROGRESS CHECKLIST</td><td>Criteria</td><td>Knowledge evidence</td><td>Date completed</td></tr>
<tr><td>C.8.3.a</td><td>What role play is and what it may help to achieve in terms of a child's development, experience and creative potential.</td><td></td></tr>
<tr><td>C.8.3.b</td><td>How to set up 'pretend' areas and activities.</td><td></td></tr>
<tr><td>C.8.3.c</td><td>How to follow a theme through role play.</td><td></td></tr>
<tr><td>C.8.3.d</td><td>The reasons why it is desirable to follow the child's lead and experiences.</td><td></td></tr>
<tr><td>C.8.3.e</td><td>How gender and cultural stereotypes may be expressed in children's role play and how to counteract this.</td><td></td></tr>
<tr><td>C.8.3.f</td><td>How to identify which equipment and materials reflect children's own cultural backgrounds and extend their knowledge of other cultural groupings.</td><td></td></tr>
</table>

## USEFUL BOOKS

*Special Issues in Child Care.* M. O'Hagan and M. Smith (1993) Bailliere Tindall.
*Just Playing.* Janet R. Moyles (1989) Open University Press.

## PORTFOLIO ACTIVITY SUMMARY

| Criteria | Portfolio page reference | 0–1 | 1–4 | 4–7 |
|---|---|---|---|---|
| C.8.3.b,c,f | See page 77 for Portfolio Activity | | | |

C.8.3.a      What is 'role/pretend' play?

..............................................................................................................................................

..............................................................................................................................................

### C.8.3.b,c,f Portfolio Activity

*Plan a theme which helps to develop the role/pretend play of a child. Set up an area or an activity linked to the theme. The equipment/materials should reflect the child's cultural background. Describe how effective and activity/area was.*

C.8.3.d    Why is it important to follow the child's lead and experiences during the role play?

..............................................................................................................................

..............................................................................................................................

..............................................................................................................................

..............................................................................................................................

C.8.3.e    What could the child care and education worker provide in the home corner which would encourage anti-discriminatory practice? Give THREE examples.

..............................................................................................................................

..............................................................................................................................

..............................................................................................................................

# C.8.4 Set out equipment for manipulative play

| PROGRESS CHECKLIST | Criteria | Knowledge evidence | Date completed |
|---|---|---|---|
| | C.8.4.a | The differences between fine and gross manipulative play. | |
| | C.8.4.b | How to identify which equipment and materials for gross and fine manipulative play are appropriate to children at various levels of development. | |
| | C.8.4.c | A selection of special equipment and how to adapt equipment for children with special needs. | |
| | C.8.4.d | How to set out the equipment attractively and to vary its presentation in order to stimulate interest. | |

## USEFUL BOOKS

*Special Issues in Child Care.* M. O'Hagan and M. Smith (1993) Balliere Tindall.

## PORTFOLIO ACTIVITY SUMMARY

| Criteria | Portfolio page reference | 0–1 | 1–4 | 4–7 |
|---|---|---|---|---|
| C.8.4.b, c&d | See page 79 for Portfolio Activity | | | |

C.8.4.a    Explain the difference between fine and gross manipulative play.

.................................................................................................................

.................................................................................................................

.................................................................................................................

.................................................................................................................

### C.8.4.b,c&d Portfolio Activity

*Plan and implement ONE activity which promotes fine manipulative play and ONE activity which promotes gross manipulative play with a child and/or group of children. Explain how ONE of the activities could be adapted for a child with a specific disability. Name the disability. Describe how effective the activities were.*

# C.8.5 Set out a selection of books to interest children

<table>
<tr><td rowspan="8" style="writing-mode: vertical-lr;">PROGRESS CHECKLIST</td><td>Criteria</td><td>Knowledge evidence</td><td>Date completed</td></tr>
<tr><td>C.8.5.a</td><td>Where to locate appropriate books including use of libraries available to the child care/education setting.</td><td></td></tr>
<tr><td>C.8.5.b</td><td>A variety of different types of books and their uses e.g. story books, fact books themes, sensory, picture books etc.</td><td></td></tr>
<tr><td>C.8.5.c</td><td>How to set out books attractively.</td><td></td></tr>
<tr><td>C.8.5.d</td><td>The sequences of child development and the appropriateness of different types of books to the particular level.</td><td></td></tr>
<tr><td>C.8.5.e</td><td>The reasons why it is important to provide books with positive images and which are non-discriminatory.</td><td></td></tr>
<tr><td>C.8.5.f</td><td>The importance and uses of books in different languages and different illustrative styles.</td><td></td></tr>
<tr><td>C.8.5.g</td><td>How to make a comfortable, attractive area for children to use books.</td><td></td></tr>
</table>

## USEFUL BOOKS

*Five to Eight.* Dorothy Butler (1986) Bodley Head Ltd.

| PORTFOLIO ACTIVITY SUMMARY | | | | |
|---|---|---|---|---|
| **Criteria** | **Portfolio page reference** | **0–1** | **1–4** | **4–7** |
| C.8.5.b&d | See page 81 for Portfolio Activity | | | |
| C.8.5.g | See page 81 for Portfolio Activity | | | |

C.8.5.a    Where can the child care and education worker find books that would be appropriate for the children? Give THREE examples.

.....................................................................................................

.....................................................................................................

.....................................................................................................

### C.8.5.b&d Portfolio Activity

*Provide evidence of a variety of types of books that have been used with different ages of children. They should include factual or information books and fiction books, picture books etc. Explain why they are appropriate for the chosen age group.*

C.8.5.c    List FIVE factors that may be considered when displaying books in an attractive way.

.....................................................................................................

.....................................................................................................

.....................................................................................................

.....................................................................................................

.....................................................................................................

C.8.5.e    Why is it important to provide children with books that show positive images and which are non-discriminatory?

.....................................................................................................

.....................................................................................................

C.8.5.f    Why is it important to use books which are printed in different languages and which have different illustrations?

.....................................................................................................

.....................................................................................................

### C.8.5.g Portfolio Activity

*Describe how you made an area within the work setting comfortable and attractive for the children to use books in.*

# C.8.6 Clear away activities and store equipment

<table>
<tr><td rowspan="7" style="writing-mode:vertical-rl">PROGRESS CHECKLIST</td><td>Criteria</td><td>Knowledge evidence</td><td>Date completed</td></tr>
<tr><td>C.8.6.a</td><td>Where and how to store equipment safely and securely.</td><td></td></tr>
<tr><td>C.8.6.b</td><td>How to encourage children to help in clearing away and the importance of giving them responsibility.</td><td></td></tr>
<tr><td>C.8.6.c</td><td>How to make clearing away fun.</td><td></td></tr>
<tr><td>C.8.6.d</td><td>The importance of effective labelling, easily accessible storage (at children's level wherever possible) inventories and reporting of stock levels, equipment faults etc.</td><td></td></tr>
<tr><td>C.8.6.e</td><td>Routines for ensuring hygiene and maintenance of equipment and storage areas.</td><td></td></tr>
<tr><td>C.8.6.c</td><td>Which materials are subject to deterioration and how to prevent or delay this.</td><td></td></tr>
</table>

## USEFUL BOOKS

*A Curriculum for the Pre-school Child.* Audrey Curtis (1986) NFER Nelson.

| PORTFOLIO ACTIVITY SUMMARY | | 0–1 | 1–4 | 4–7 |
|---|---|---|---|---|
| **Criteria** | **Portfolio page reference** | | | |
| C.8.6.a&d | See page 83 for Portfolio Activity | | | |
| C.8.6.e | See page 83 for Portfolio Activity | | | |

### C.8.6.a&d Portfolio Activity

*Describe where and how the equipment in the work setting is stored. This should include:*

>    (a) *the importance of labelling;*
>    (b) *safety and security;*
>    (c) *easy access for the adult and child;*
>    (d) *methods of recording stock.*

C.8.6.b    Why is it important to encourage children to help tidy up?

.......................................................................................................................................

.......................................................................................................................................

.......................................................................................................................................

.......................................................................................................................................

C.8.6.c    Describe how the child care and education worker can make tidying up fun for the children.

.......................................................................................................................................

.......................................................................................................................................

.......................................................................................................................................

.......................................................................................................................................

### C.8.6.e Portfolio Activity

*Describe the work setting's routine for ensuring that the equipment is well maintained AND hygienic.*

C.8.6.f    Name FIVE materials that are used in the work setting which are likely to deteriorate. For EACH material explain how this may be prevented or delayed.

.......................................................................................................................................

.......................................................................................................................................

.......................................................................................................................................

.......................................................................................................................................

.......................................................................................................................................

# C.9 WORK WITH YOUNG CHILDREN UNIT WIDE KNOWLEDGE

| | Criteria | Knowledge evidence | Date completed |
|---|---|---|---|
| **P R O G R E S S   C H E C K L I S T** | C.9.a | Basic knowledge of children's development 6 weeks to 8 years. | |
| | C.9.b | How young children learn and the importance of play, active exploration and discovery. | |
| | C.9.c | How to communicate with and listen to young children. | |
| | C.9.d | The role of the adult in supporting children's learning and development. | |
| | C.9.e | Ways in which gender and other forms of stereotyping can affect children's participation in activities and how to counteract this in work with children. | |

## USEFUL BOOKS

*Special Issues in Child Care.* M. O'Hagan and M. Smith (1993) Bailliere Tindall.
*Babies and Young Children Book 1 Development 0–7 years.* Beaver *et al*, (1994) Stanley Thornes.
*A Practical Guide to Activities with Young Children.* Jill Frankel and Christine Hobart (1994) Stanley Thornes.
*Caring for the under 8s.* Jennie and Lance Lindon (1993) Macmillan.

## PORTFOLIO ACTIVITY SUMMARY

| Criteria | Portfolio page reference | 0–1 | 1–4 | 4–7 |
|---|---|---|---|---|
| C.9.c | See page 88 for Portfolio Activity | | | |

# C.9 Work with young children

C.9.a     (*This work has been covered in the introductory unit.*)

C.9.b     'How do children learn?' Many people have tried to answer this question. Briefly describe the work of B.F. Skinner in relation to children's learning.

..................................................................................................................................

..................................................................................................................................

..................................................................................................................................

..................................................................................................................................

..................................................................................................................................

..................................................................................................................................

..................................................................................................................................

..................................................................................................................................

..................................................................................................................................

..................................................................................................................................

Briefly describe the work of Albert Bandura in relation to children's learning.

..................................................................................................................................

..................................................................................................................................

..................................................................................................................................

..................................................................................................................................

..................................................................................................................................

..................................................................................................................................

..................................................................................................................................

..................................................................................................................................

..................................................................................................

..................................................................................................

(*NB*  *There are a lot of books on this subject, but those suggested will provide you with sufficient information*)

How do you think children learn? What conclusions have you made about the way in which children learn?

..................................................................................................

..................................................................................................

..................................................................................................

..................................................................................................

..................................................................................................

..................................................................................................

Why is play important for children's learning?

..................................................................................................

..................................................................................................

..................................................................................................

..................................................................................................

..................................................................................................

..................................................................................................

..................................................................................................

..................................................................................................

..................................................................................................

..................................................................................................

**C.9.c**    Why is it important to listen to children?

........................................................................................................................

........................................................................................................................

........................................................................................................................

........................................................................................................................

........................................................................................................................

........................................................................................................................

........................................................................................................................

........................................................................................................................

........................................................................................................................

........................................................................................................................

........................................................................................................................

Explain the advice you would give to an inexperienced member of staff on how to listen to children.

........................................................................................................................

........................................................................................................................

........................................................................................................................

........................................................................................................................

........................................................................................................................

........................................................................................................................

........................................................................................................................

........................................................................................................................

Read the two questions below. Which question will encourage a child to talk? Give reasons for your choice.

(*a*) 'Would you like an apple or an orange?'
(*b*) 'What did you do yesterday?'

........................................................................................

........................................................................................

........................................................................................

........................................................................................

### C.9.c Portfolio Activity

*Observe an adult talking with a child. Note the type of questions that are asked and describe how effective they were in encouraging the child to talk.*

### C.9.c Portfolio Activity

*Design a leaflet for parents which explains ways in which children can be encouraged to communicate.*

C.9.d    Describe the role of the adult in supporting children's learning and development.

........................................................................................

........................................................................................

........................................................................................

........................................................................................

........................................................................................

........................................................................................

C.9.e    How can gender stereotyping affect a child's participation in activities?

........................................................................................

..................................................................................................

..................................................................................................

..................................................................................................

How can the child care and education worker discourage gender stereotyping?
Give THREE practical examples.

..................................................................................................

..................................................................................................

..................................................................................................

..................................................................................................

..................................................................................................

..................................................................................................

# C.9.1 Participate with children in a singing/music session

PROGRESS CHECKLIST

| Criteria | Knowledge evidence | Date completed |
|----------|-------------------|----------------|
| C.9.1.a | A selection of songs and musical activities, to cover the range. | |
| C.9.1.b | The approximate attention span of children of different ages. | |
| C.9.1.c | Types of songs which are or are not likely to work with groups of different size. | |
| C.9.1.d | Appropriate instruments (including home-made) and how to use them. | |
| C.9.1.e | The role of music and songs in promoting children's learning and development. | |
| C.9.1.f | How to adapt/change words of traditional songs and rhymes in order to avoid stereotyping. | |
| C.9.1.g | How to adapt/design sessions to encourage participation of children with hearing impairment. | |

## USEFUL BOOKS

There is a wide range of books available on this topic. It is worth visiting your local book shop or library.

| PORTFOLIO ACTIVITY SUMMARY | | | | |
|----------|-------------------|-----|-----|-----|
| Criteria | Portfolio page reference | 0–1 | 1–4 | 4–7 |
| C.9.1.a&c | See page 91 for Portfolio Activity | | | |
| C.9.1.c | See page 91 for Portfolio Activity | | | |

## C.9.1.a & C.9.1.c Portfolio Activity

*Plan and implement at least ONE musical activity with a small or large group of children aged 1–4 years or 4–7 years.*

C.9.1.b    Look at the statements below, and number them according to the stages of attention span you would expect a child to progress through. (The earliest stage would be 1.)

☐ Concentrates on what is being done and blocks everything else out.
☐ Easily distracted.
☐ The child is able to leave the activity to listen to instructions and then go back to the activity.
☐ The child is able to leave the activity to listen to the instruction but he/she often needs help to return to the activity.

## C.9.1.c Portfolio Activity

*Make a collection of songs and rhymes to be used with children from 1–7 years 11 months of age. Give reasons for your choice.*

C.9.1.d    Name FIVE musical instruments that would be appropriate for children to use in small groups. How would they play each one?

...........................................................................................................................................

...........................................................................................................................................

...........................................................................................................................................

...........................................................................................................................................

...........................................................................................................................................

C.9.1.e    Describe the role of music and songs in promoting children's learning and development.

...........................................................................................................................................

...........................................................................................................................................

...........................................................................................................................................

...........................................................................................................................................

..................................................................................................

..................................................................................................

..................................................................................................

..................................................................................................

..................................................................................................

..................................................................................................

C.9.1.f    Using an example of your choice, show how you would change the words of a
           traditional song or rhyme to avoid stereotyping.

..................................................................................................

..................................................................................................

..................................................................................................

..................................................................................................

..................................................................................................

..................................................................................................

C.9.1.g    Give a brief description of a musical activity that a child care and education
           worker could use with a small group of children. Explain how the activity
           could be adapted to encourage a child with a hearing impairment to
           participate.

..................................................................................................

..................................................................................................

..................................................................................................

..................................................................................................

..................................................................................................

..................................................................................................

..................................................................................................

# C.9.2 Tell/read a story to children

| | Criteria | Knowledge evidence | Date completed |
|---|---|---|---|
| **PROGRESS CHECKLIST** | C.9.2.a | A selection of books and stories to cover the range and why they are suitable. | |
| | C.9.2.b | Children's possible emotional responses to stories. | |
| | C.9.2.c | The role of books and stories in promoting children's learning and development | |
| | C.9.2.d | How literature and illustrative styles vary across culture and why it is important to show children books in different languages and styles. | |
| | C.9.2.e | How positive images in books and stories are important to children's developing sense of identity and feelings of self-worth. | |
| | C.9.2.f | How to review books and stories in preparation for a story session. | |
| | C.9.2.g | How to adapt/design a story telling session to enable the participation of children with sensory impairment. | |

## USEFUL BOOKS

*Five to Eight.* Dorothy Butler (1986) Bodley Head Ltd.

| PORTFOLIO ACTIVITY SUMMARY | | | | |
|---|---|---|---|---|
| Criteria | Portfolio page reference | 0–1 | 1–4 | 4–7 |
| C.9.2.a | See page 94 for Portfolio Activity | | | |
| C.9.2.b | See page 94 for Portfolio Activity | | | |
| C.9.2.f | See page 95 for Portfolio Activity | | | |

**C.9.2.a Portfolio Activity**

*Plan and implement a storytelling session with children aged 1–4 years and/or 4–7 years 11 months. The session can be with an individual child, or a group of children.*

 **C.9.2.b Portfolio Activity**

*Observe a story session and write an account of the emotional responses made by the children during the session.*

C.9.2.c    Describe the role of books and stories in promoting children's learning and development.

...................................................................................................................................

...................................................................................................................................

...................................................................................................................................

...................................................................................................................................

...................................................................................................................................

...................................................................................................................................

...................................................................................................................................

...................................................................................................................................

...................................................................................................................................

...................................................................................................................................

...................................................................................................................................

C.9.2.d    Describe TWO differences that may be seen in books from different cultures.

...................................................................................................................................

...................................................................................................................................

...................................................................................................................................

Why is it important to show children books from different cultures?

C.9.2.e    Describe how the positive images in books can give children a feeling of self-identity and self-worth?

 ### *C.9.2.f Portfolio Activity*

*Design a checklist which you could use to review books and stories in preparation for a story session. Review FIVE books in your checklist.*

C.9.2.g    Explain how the child care and education worker can ensure that a child with a sensory impairment can participate in a story session.

# C.9.3 Set out objects of interest and examine them with children

| | Criteria | Knowledge evidence | Date completed |
|---|---|---|---|
| **PROGRESS CHECKLIST** | C.9.3.a | Why and how examination and sensory exploration of objects of interest can be used to promote children's learning and development. | |
| | C.9.3.b | How to build on children's natural curiosity and how not to stifle it. | |
| | C.9.3.c | How to enable children with sensory impairment to explore and examine objects effectively. | |
| | C.9.3.d | The sorts of objects and materials which reflect the cultural background of the children in the group and others which can be used to extend their understanding of other cultures. | |

## USEFUL BOOKS

*Caring for Young Children.* Jennie and Lance Lindon (1994) Macmillan.

C.9.3.a    How can children learn from handling interesting objects?

.................................................................................................................................

.................................................................................................................................

.................................................................................................................................

.................................................................................................................................

C.9.3.b    How can the adult encourage the child's curiosity?

.................................................................................................................................

.................................................................................................................................

..........................................................................................................

..........................................................................................................

C.9.3.c    Describe how the child care and education worker can enable a child with a sensory impairment to explore and examine objects?

..........................................................................................................

..........................................................................................................

..........................................................................................................

..........................................................................................................

C.9.3.d    List FOUR different objects and/or materials which reflect the cultural background of the children in the work setting.

..........................................................................................................

..........................................................................................................

..........................................................................................................

..........................................................................................................

List FOUR different objects and/or materials which could be used to extend the children's understanding of other cultures.

..........................................................................................................

..........................................................................................................

..........................................................................................................

..........................................................................................................

# C.9.4 Assist children with a cooking activity

<table>
<tr><td rowspan="7" style="writing-mode: vertical-lr;">PROGRESS CHECKLIST</td><td>**Criteria**</td><td>**Knowledge evidence**</td><td>**Date completed**</td></tr>
<tr><td>C.9.4.a</td><td>Hygiene requirements (including need to cool and cover food; time for which ingredients can be stored safely).</td><td></td></tr>
<tr><td>C.9.4.b</td><td>General principles of healthy eating and 'healthy eating' recipes.</td><td></td></tr>
<tr><td>C.9.4.c</td><td>A variety of recipes suitable for making with children in a group including examples from different cultures.</td><td></td></tr>
<tr><td>C.9.4.d</td><td>Demands of different cooking processes and recipes in relation to children of different ages and levels of development.</td><td></td></tr>
<tr><td>C.9.4.e</td><td>How to adapt cooking activities to enable participation of children with special needs.</td><td></td></tr>
<tr><td>C.9.4.f</td><td>The potential of cooking activities for promoting different aspects of children's learning and development.</td><td></td></tr>
</table>

## USEFUL BOOKS

*Essential Food Hygiene.* Dr R.J. Donaldson (1988) Royal Society of Health.
*Food and Nutrition.* Anita Tull (1993) Oxford University Press.

| PORTFOLIO ACTIVITY SUMMARY | | | | |
|---|---|---|---|---|
| **Criteria** | **Portfolio page reference** | **0–1** | **1–4** | **4–7** |
| C.9.4.c, d&e | See page 99 for Portfolio Activity | | | |

C.9.4.a&b  This work will be assessed in C.2.

## C.9.4.c,d&e Portfolio Activity

*Plan and implement a cooking activity with a child or group of children. The plan should include a detailed recipe. In your evaluation explain the difficulties the children had during the cooking process due to their level of development. Explain how cooking activities could be adapted to enable a child with a disability to participate.*

C.9.4.f    How can a cooking activity promote the development of the child?

.......................................................................................................................................

.......................................................................................................................................

.......................................................................................................................................

.......................................................................................................................................

.......................................................................................................................................

.......................................................................................................................................

# C.9.5 Play a game with children

| | Criteria | Knowledge evidence | Date completed |
|---|---|---|---|
| **PROGRESS CHECKLIST** | C.9.5.a | The role that table top games can play in increasing a child's understanding of number matching and sequence. | |
| | C.9.5.b | How playing games with children can be part of an overall theme assisting children's development. | |
| | C.9.5.c | How to devise and improvise children's games. | |
| | C.9.5.d | Selection of games to cover the stated range. | |
| | C.9.5.e | The effects of competitive games and losing on children's behaviour and self-esteem. | |
| | C.9.5.f | The potential role of traditional games in gender stereotyping and how to counteract this. | |
| | C.9.5.g | The sequence of development of children's play with particular reference to parallel play, cooperative play, turn-taking, sharing and the ability to cope with rules. | |
| | C.9.5.h | How to handle children who are disruptive and non-cooperative and those who don't want to join in. | |
| | C.9.5.i | How to adapt games to enable the participation of children with special needs. | |

## USEFUL BOOKS

*Special Issues in Child Care.* M. O'Hagan and M. Smith (1993) Bailliere Tindall.

| PORTFOLIO ACTIVITY SUMMARY | | 0–1 | 1–4 | 4–7 |
|---|---|---|---|---|
| **Criteria** | **Portfolio page reference** | | | |
| C.9.5.b | See below for Portfolio Activity | | | |
| C.9.5c&d | See below for Portfolio Activity | | | |
| C.9.5.h | See page 102 for Portfolio Activity | | | |

C.9.5.a    How can a child care and education worker use table top games to develop a child's understanding of number, matching and sequence?

..................................................................................................................................

..................................................................................................................................

..................................................................................................................................

..................................................................................................................................

 *C.9.5.b Portfolio Activity*

*Plan a theme which will assist the overall development of the child and show how playing games can be included.*

 *C.9.5.c & d Portfolio Activity*

*Design a child's table top game. Use it with an individual child or group of children and evaluate its effectiveness.*

C.9.5.e    When children play completitive games, what effect could losing have on:

   (*a*) their behaviour;

..................................................................................................................................

..................................................................................................................................

..................................................................................................................................

   (*b*) their self-esteem.

..................................................................................................................................

..................................................................................................

..................................................................................................

C.9.5.f    List THREE games which promote gender stereotyping. For EACH game explain how they could be changed to prevent this.

..................................................................................................

..................................................................................................

..................................................................................................

..................................................................................................

..................................................................................................

..................................................................................................

C.9.5.g    Place the following types of play in order, with number 1 being used by the youngest child.

☐ Spectator/on-looking      ☐ Cooperative play
☐ Parallel play             ☐ Solitary
☐ Play game with rules      ☐ Associative

### C.9.5.h Portfolio Activity

*Write a short description of your own personal effectiveness in encouraging children to participate when they did not want to AND how you dealt with children who were being disruptive.*

C.9.5.i    Describe how the child care and education worker could adapt a game to ensure that a child with special needs could participate. Give examples.

..................................................................................................

..................................................................................................

..................................................................................................

..................................................................................................

..................................................................................................

# C.9.6 Participate in a talking and listening activity with children

| | Criteria | Knowledge evidence | Date completed |
|---|---|---|---|
| **PROGRESS CHECKLIST** | C.9.6.a | Appropriate talking and listening games and activities for children of different ages and levels of development. | |
| | C.9.6.b | How children develop communication skills and how to promote their development. | |
| | C.9.6.c | How layout and physical conditions can affect communication. | |
| | C.9.6.d | A variety of common communication difficulties in young children. | |
| | C.9.6.e | How to adapt talking and listening games and activities to enable the participation of children with hearing impairment. | |

## USEFUL BOOKS

*A Curriculum for the Pre-school Child.* Audrey Curtis (1986) NFER Nelson.
*Children with Speech and Language Difficulties.* Alec Webster and Christine McConnell
  (1987) Cassell Educational Ltd.

## PORTFOLIO ACTIVITY SUMMARY

| Criteria | Portfolio page reference | 0–1 | 1–4 | 4–7 |
|---|---|---|---|---|
| C.9.6.a | See page 104 for Portfolio Activity | | | |
| C.9.6.c | See page 105 for Portfolio Activity | | | |

## C.9.6.a Portfolio Activity

*Plan and implement a talking and/or listening game for children aged 1–4 and/or 4–7 years 11 months.*

C.9.6.b      How do children learn to communicate?

.......................................................................................................................................

.......................................................................................................................................

.......................................................................................................................................

.......................................................................................................................................

.......................................................................................................................................

.......................................................................................................................................

.......................................................................................................................................

.......................................................................................................................................

.......................................................................................................................................

.......................................................................................................................................

.......................................................................................................................................

How can the child care and education worker help to promote the communication skills of children?

.......................................................................................................................................

.......................................................................................................................................

.......................................................................................................................................

.......................................................................................................................................

.......................................................................................................................................

.......................................................................................................................................

..................................................................................................................................

..................................................................................................................................

..................................................................................................................................

..................................................................................................................................

..................................................................................................................................

..................................................................................................................................

### *C.9.6.c Portfolio Activity*

*Observe a child in the work setting and describe how the layout and physical conditions can affect the child's communication skills.*

C.9.6.d    List **THREE** common communication difficulties that a child may experience.

..................................................................................................................................

..................................................................................................................................

..................................................................................................................................

C.9.6.e    Describe how the child care and education worker may adapt a talking or listening game which could allow a child with a hearing impairment to participate.

..................................................................................................................................

..................................................................................................................................

..................................................................................................................................

..................................................................................................................................

..................................................................................................................................

..................................................................................................................................

# C.9.7 Support children's involvement in activities

<table>
<tr><th rowspan="10" style="writing-mode: vertical-rl">PROGRESS CHECKLIST</th><th>Criteria</th><th>Knowledge evidence</th><th>Date completed</th></tr>
<tr><td>C.9.7.a</td><td>How to support and encourage children in their activities without disrupting their play or detracting from their overall control/self-reliance.</td><td></td></tr>
<tr><td>C.9.7.b</td><td>The role of types of activities stated in the range in promoting children's learning and development and why, when and how adult intervention might be necessary.</td><td></td></tr>
<tr><td>C.9.7.c</td><td>Particular health and safety considerations of the various common types of activities for children in childcare and educational settings.</td><td></td></tr>
<tr><td>C.9.7.d</td><td>The importance of independence, self-direction and task achievement with minimal assistance in developing children's self-esteem and self-confidence.</td><td></td></tr>
</table>

## USEFUL BOOKS

*Time to Play in Early Childhood Education.* Tina Bruce (1991) Hodder and Stoughton.
*Working with Young Children.* Jennie Laishley (1987) Hodder and Stoughton.

C.9.7.a    How can the child care and education worker support a child during an activity without disrupting the play?

.......................................................................................................................................

.......................................................................................................................................

.......................................................................................................................................

.......................................................................................................................................

.......................................................................................................................................

.......................................................................................................................................

C.9.7.b    Describe how the following activities can encourage a child's development:

(*a*) adult directed/structured activities;

..........................................................................................................................

..........................................................................................................................

..........................................................................................................................

..........................................................................................................................

(*b*) spontaneous/child-initiated activities;

..........................................................................................................................

..........................................................................................................................

..........................................................................................................................

..........................................................................................................................

(*c*) physical play with large equipment;

..........................................................................................................................

..........................................................................................................................

..........................................................................................................................

..........................................................................................................................

(*d*) everyday routines.

..........................................................................................................................

..........................................................................................................................

..........................................................................................................................

..........................................................................................................................

C.9.7.c    Describe what health and safety considerations need to be taken into account in the following activities. Give TWO different examples for EACH activity:

(*a*) music session;

..........................................................................................................................

..............................................................................................................

..............................................................................................................

..............................................................................................................

(b) story session;

..............................................................................................................

..............................................................................................................

..............................................................................................................

(c) displays/interest tables;

..............................................................................................................

..............................................................................................................

..............................................................................................................

(d) cooking activity;

..............................................................................................................

..............................................................................................................

..............................................................................................................

(e) table top games;

..............................................................................................................

..............................................................................................................

..............................................................................................................

(f) talking and listening.

..............................................................................................................

..............................................................................................

..............................................................................................

..............................................................................................

C.9.7.d    Why is it important to allow the child to work on an activity by himself/herself
with the minimal amount of help from the adult?

..............................................................................................

..............................................................................................

..............................................................................................

..............................................................................................

..............................................................................................

..............................................................................................

# E.1 MAINTAIN A CHILD ORIENTATED ENVIRONMENT
## UNIT WIDE KNOWLEDGE

| | Criteria | Knowledge evidence | Date completed |
|---|---|---|---|
| PROGRESS CHECKLIST | E.1.a | The role of the environment in children's learning and in meeting their needs. | |
| | E.1.b | The relationship between the home environment and the care/education environment. | |

## USEFUL BOOKS

*Caring for children under 8s.* Jennie and Lance Lindon (1993) Macmillan.

# E.1 Maintain a child orientated environment

E.1.a    How can the environment assist in a child's learning?

..............................................................................................................

..............................................................................................................

..............................................................................................................

..............................................................................................................

..............................................................................................................

..............................................................................................................

How can the environment meet the needs of a child?

..............................................................................................................

..............................................................................................................

..............................................................................................................

..............................................................................................................

..............................................................................................................

..............................................................................................................

E.1.b    Describe the relationship between the home environment and the
care/education environment.

..............................................................................................................

..............................................................................................................

..............................................................................................................

..............................................................................................................

..............................................................................................................

..............................................................................................................

# E.1.1 Maintain the physical environment for young children

<table>
<tr><td rowspan="8" style="writing-mode: vertical-rl">PROGRESS CHECKLIST</td><td>Criteria</td><td>Knowledge evidence</td><td>Date completed</td></tr>
<tr><td>E.1.1.a</td><td>Safety requirements with respect to heating, lighting, access including content of current borough/council regulations and documents.</td><td></td></tr>
<tr><td>E.1.1.b</td><td>Safety procedures for emergencies including fire.</td><td></td></tr>
<tr><td>E.1.1.c</td><td>Ways in which the layout of furniture and equipment can:<br>1) encourage or discourage different kinds of activity, including individual work;<br>2) increase or decrease children's feelings of security;<br>3) make it physically easier/harder to engage in an activity, and clear up mess/change activities.</td><td></td></tr>
<tr><td>E.1.1.d</td><td>Entry to and layout within a setting may create access problems for the physically handicapped.</td><td></td></tr>
<tr><td>E.1.1.e</td><td>The modifications required to the environment to cater for children with a variety of special needs.</td><td></td></tr>
<tr><td>E.1.1.f</td><td>The benefits to young children of being able to participate in decision making.</td><td></td></tr>
<tr><td>E.1.1.g</td><td>Children's need to explore their environment in safety and security.</td><td></td></tr>
</table>

## USEFUL BOOKS

*Accident Prevention in Day Care and Play Settings* (1992) NES Arnold.

## PORTFOLIO ACTIVITY SUMMARY

| Criteria | Portfolio page reference | 0–1 | 1–4 | 4–7 |
|---|---|---|---|---|
| E.1.1.b | See page 113 for Portfolio Activity | | | |

E.1.1.a    Describe the local regulations for the safety requirements of the work setting with regard to:

(*a*) heating;

.......................................................................................................................

.......................................................................................................................

.......................................................................................................................

(*b*) lighting;

.......................................................................................................................

.......................................................................................................................

.......................................................................................................................

(*c*) ventilation;

.......................................................................................................................

.......................................................................................................................

.......................................................................................................................

(*d*) access.

.......................................................................................................................

.......................................................................................................................

.......................................................................................................................

 ### E.1.1.b Portfolio Activity

*Describe the fire drill procedures in the work setting.*

Describe how the child care and education worker could prepare the children for the fire drill procedure. Give THREE strategies.

.......................................................................................................................

.......................................................................................................................

.......................................................................................................................

..............................................................................................

..............................................................................................

..............................................................................................

The fire alarm has sounded and a child has become hysterical. What should the child care and education worker do? Give TWO examples.

..............................................................................................

..............................................................................................

..............................................................................................

..............................................................................................

E.1.1.c   How can the layout of furniture and equipment in the work setting:

(a) encourage different types of activities;

..............................................................................................

..............................................................................................

..............................................................................................

(b) discourage different types of activities;

..............................................................................................

..............................................................................................

..............................................................................................

(c) increase the child's feeling of security;

..............................................................................................

..............................................................................................

..............................................................................................

(d) decrease the child's feeling of security;

..............................................................................................

..............................................................................................

..........................................................................................................

(*e*) make it physically easier to take part in an activity;

..........................................................................................................

..........................................................................................................

..........................................................................................................

(*f*) make it physically harder to take part in an activity.

..........................................................................................................

..........................................................................................................

..........................................................................................................

E.1.1.d  Describe how entry to the unit and the layout of the activities may create access difficulties for a child with a disability.

..........................................................................................................

..........................................................................................................

..........................................................................................................

..........................................................................................................

..........................................................................................................

E.1.1.e  Describe how EACH of the difficulties stated in E.1.1.d might be overcome.

..........................................................................................................

..........................................................................................................

..........................................................................................................

..........................................................................................................

..........................................................................................................

..........................................................................................................

E.1.1.f    How can a child benefit from being able to make decisions within the work
setting?

........................................................................................................

........................................................................................................

........................................................................................................

........................................................................................................

E.1.1.g    Why does a child need to be able to explore his/her environment in safety and
security?

........................................................................................................

........................................................................................................

........................................................................................................

........................................................................................................

# E.1.2 Maintain an attractive and stimulating environment for young children

| | Criteria | Knowledge evidence | Date completed |
|---|---|---|---|
| **PROGRESS CHECKLIST** | E.1.2.a | Principles of display; how to arrange materials to attract children's attention, how to make it easier for them to absorb content. | |
| | E.1.2.b | A variety of techniques for mounting work and displaying it attractively. | |
| | E.1.2.c | The names of common plants and materials found in the vicinity. | |
| | E.1.2.d | How to care for plants. | |

## USEFUL BOOKS

*Creative Display and Environment.* Margaret Jackson (1993) Hodder and Stoughton.

| PORTFOLIO ACTIVITY SUMMARY | | | | |
|---|---|---|---|---|
| Criteria | Portfolio page reference | 0–1 | 1–4 | 4–7 |
| E.1.2.a&b | See below for Portfolio Activity | | | |
| E.1.2.c | See page 118 for Portfolio Activity | | | |
| E.1.2.d | See page 118 for Portfolio Activity | | | |

 ### E.1.2.a&b Portfolio Activity

*Provide evidence in your portfolio of TWO displays that you have arranged in the work setting. Use TWO different display techniques. Explain:*

    (a) *how you arranged the materials in order to attract the children's attention;*
    (b) *how you helped the children absorb the information.*

### E.1.2.c Portfolio Activity

*Illustrate and name FIVE common flowers, FIVE common trees and FIVE natural materials that may be found near the work setting.*

 ### E.1.2.d Portfolio Activity

*Design a series of cards which will explain to the children how to care for plants in the work setting. The cards may or may not have words on them.*

# *E.1.3 Maintain a reassuring environment for children*

| | Criteria | Knowledge evidence | Date completed |
|---|---|---|---|
| **PROGRESS CHECKLIST** | E.1.3.a | Common sources of fear amongst babies, toddlers, pre-schoolers, including fear of separation. (This covers simple knowledge of common stages/fears – enough to anticipate/recognise, but nothing more detailed.) | |
| | E.1.3.b | Awareness of manifestations of fear. Ways of reassuring/dealing with fears including use of comfort objects. | |
| | E.1.3.c | Existence of marked differences among children in liking for/need of physical comfort. | |
| | E.1.3.d | A variety of equipment and materials, including kitchen and washing equipment and fabrics, typical of a range of cultural backgrounds. | |

## USEFUL BOOKS

*Special Issues in Child Care.* M. O'Hagan and M. Smith (1993) Bailliere Tindall.

## PORTFOLIO ACTIVITY SUMMARY

| Criteria | Portfolio page reference | 0–1 | 1–4 | 4–7 |
|---|---|---|---|---|
| E.1.3.c | See page 120 for Portfolio Activity | | | |

E.1.3.a    List TWO different common sources of fear for EACH of the following stages of development:

(*a*) babies;

....................................................................................................................

....................................................................................................................

(*b*) toddlers;

.......................................................................................................................

.......................................................................................................................

(*c*) pre-school.

.......................................................................................................................

.......................................................................................................................

E.1.3.b    How can the child care and education worker help a child deal with a fear that he/she may have? Give TWO examples. State the type of fear and age of the child.

.......................................................................................................................

.......................................................................................................................

.......................................................................................................................

.......................................................................................................................

 ### E.1.3.c Portfolio Activity

*Some children need more physical comfort than others when distressed. Observe TWO children on TWO separate occasions in the work setting who are distressed and who are being comforted by a carer.*

E.1.3.d    Name THREE things you could give to a child from a different cultural background which would help to make him/her feel secure in the work setting.

.......................................................................................................................

.......................................................................................................................

.......................................................................................................................

# E.2 MAINTAIN THE SAFETY OF CHILDREN UNIT WIDE KNOWLEDGE

| | Criteria | Knowledge evidence | Date completed |
|---|---|---|---|
| **PROGRESS CHECKLIST** | E.2.a | Basic knowledge of children's development 6 weeks to 8 years and importance of taking account of this when considering safety arrangements. | |
| | E.2.b | Awareness of hazards within the environment e.g. traffic, pollution, strangers, animals, poison, berries, water etc. | |
| | E.2.c | The need to actively protect children from hazards and the vital role adults have in this. | |
| | E.2.d | The importance of keeping records essential to the safety of children and of ongoing consultation with the primary carer. | |
| | E.2.e | Health and safety requirements of the setting and the importance of ensuring that these are displayed and communicated clearly to other adults in the setting. | |
| | E.2.f | The responsibility of the carer with regard to protection from infectious diseases and the positive contribution immunisation can make. | |
| | E.2.g | Identify and use available resources concerned with safety to raise awareness of candidate, children and adults. | |
| | E.2.h | Provide children, parents and other adults with a positive role model with regard to safety. | |

## USEFUL BOOKS

*Babies and Young Children: Development 0–8 years.* Beaver *et al,* (1994) Stanley Thornes.

| PORTFOLIO ACTIVITY SUMMARY | | | | |
|---|---|---|---|---|
| Criteria | Portfolio page reference | 0–1 | 1–4 | 4–7 |
| E.2.a | See page 123 for Portfolio Activity | | | |
| E.2.e | See page 124 for Portfolio Activity | | | |

# E.2 Maintain the safety of children

### E.2.a Portfolio Activity

*Design a booklet for parents which explains the development of a child from 6 weeks to 8 years. It should also explain why it is important to take account of the child's development when considering safety issues.*

E.2.b    List FIVE hazards that a child may encounter in the environment.

.................................................................................................................................

.................................................................................................................................

.................................................................................................................................

.................................................................................................................................

.................................................................................................................................

E.2.c    Why is it important for an adult to protect children from potential hazards?

.................................................................................................................................

.................................................................................................................................

.................................................................................................................................

.................................................................................................................................

E.2.d    Why is it important to keep safety records?

.................................................................................................................................

.................................................................................................................................

.................................................................................................................................

.................................................................................................................................

.................................................................................................................................

### E.2.e Portfolio Activity

*What are the health and safety requirements of the work setting? Explain why it is important to display the regulations within the work setting? (**NB** You may have answered this question in C.2.e)*

E.2.f    What can the carer do to prevent infection spreading in the work setting?

.......................................................................................................................................

.......................................................................................................................................

.......................................................................................................................................

.......................................................................................................................................

.......................................................................................................................................

.......................................................................................................................................

What is the value of immunisation programmes?

.......................................................................................................................................

.......................................................................................................................................

.......................................................................................................................................

.......................................................................................................................................

.......................................................................................................................................

E.2.g    What resources are available to promote an awareness of safety issues for:

(*a*) the child;

.......................................................................................................................................

.......................................................................................................................................

.......................................................................................................................................

.......................................................................................................................................

.......................................................................................................................................

(*b*) the adult.

..............................................................................................................

..............................................................................................................

..............................................................................................................

..............................................................................................................

..............................................................................................................

If possible, include examples of leaflets etc. in your portfolio.

E.2.h     Why is it important for the adult to provide a positive role model to the child?

..............................................................................................................

..............................................................................................................

..............................................................................................................

..............................................................................................................

# E.2.1 Maintain a safe environment for children

| | Criteria | Knowledge evidence | Date completed |
|---|---|---|---|
| **PROGRESS CHECKLIST** | E.2.1.a | The importance of maintaining a hygienic environment for the safety of children. | |
| | E.2.1.b | Routine safety checks on premises/equipment are carried out and appropriate action is taken. | |
| | E.2.1.c | How to identify potential hazards and minimize the possible effects of them within the setting both indoors and outdoors. | |
| | E.2.1.d | The health and safety hazards posed by animals in the care/education setting. | |
| | E.2.1.e | The procedures for reporting and correcting any safety hazards as quickly as possible in a manner which does not undermine the confidence of children. | |
| | E.2.1.f | The importance of adhering to manufacturers' recommendations and relevant safety standards when using equipment. | |

## USEFUL BOOKS

*Accident Prevention in Day Care and Play Settings.* Pam Laidman (1992) NES Arnold.

## PORTFOLIO ACTIVITY SUMMARY

| Criteria | Portfolio page reference | 0–1 | 1–4 | 4–7 |
|---|---|---|---|---|
| E.2.1.b | See page 127 for Portfolio Activity | | | |

E.2.1.a    Why should the child care and education worker provide a hygienic
environment for the children?

..............................................................................................................................

..............................................................................................................................

..............................................................................................................................

..............................................................................................................................

### E.2.1.b Portfolio Activity

*Design a checklist that you could use when carrying out routine safety checks on equipment and work
areas. Indoor AND outdoor equipment should be included.*

E.2.1.c    List FOUR potential indoor hazards and FOUR potential outdoor hazards in
the work setting AND explain how the effects of EACH of these hazards could
be minimised.

..............................................................................................................................

..............................................................................................................................

..............................................................................................................................

..............................................................................................................................

..............................................................................................................................

..............................................................................................................................

..............................................................................................................................

..............................................................................................................................

E.2.1.d    List THREE health and safety hazards posed by animals in the work setting.

..............................................................................................................................

..............................................................................................................................

..............................................................................................................................

E.2.1.e    The nursery gate has been left open. A small group of children are running purposefully towards it. What action should the child care and education worker take?

..................................................................................................................................

..................................................................................................................................

..................................................................................................................................

..................................................................................................................................

E.2.1.f    Explain why it is important to follow the manufacturer's instructions and the relevant safety standards when using equipment.

..................................................................................................................................

..................................................................................................................................

..................................................................................................................................

..................................................................................................................................

# E.2.2 Maintain supervision of children

| | Criteria | Knowledge evidence | Date completed |
|---|---|---|---|
| **PROGRESS CHECKLIST** | E.2.2.a | The regulations concerning adult/child ratios appropriate in the setting and the importance of adhering to these. | |
| | E.2.2.b | That adult anxiety/inappropriate reactions to events are often transmitted to children and that stereotyping can prevent a child from achieving his/her potential. | |
| | E.2.2.c | The importance of policies and procedures for collection of children taking account of any special circumstances e.g. Care Orders. | |

## USEFUL BOOKS

*An Introduction to the Children Act.* (1989) H.M.S.O.
*Making Sense of the Children Act.* N. Allen (1991) Longman.

| PORTFOLIO ACTIVITY SUMMARY | | | | |
|---|---|---|---|---|
| Criteria | Portfolio page reference | 0–1 | 1–4 | 4–7 |
| E.2.2.a | See below for Portfolio Activity | | | |
| E.2.2.c | See page 130 for Portfolio Activity | | | |

 ## E.2.2.a Portfolio Activity

*Design a chart which shows the adult/child ratios at different ages for the following work settings:*

> (a) *childminders with babies and pre-school children;*
> (b) *play groups.*

E.2.2.a    Why is it important to follow the regulations relating to adult/child ratios in the work setting?

...............................................................................................

...............................................................................................

...............................................................................................

...............................................................................................

**E.2.2.b**    What effect can an anxious adult have on a child in the work setting?

...............................................................................................

...............................................................................................

...............................................................................................

...............................................................................................

 ### E.2.2.c Portfolio Activity

*Describe the safety rules and procedures for collecting children from the work setting. This should include a description relevant to Child Care Orders.*

**E.2.2.c**    Why it is important to have procedures for the collection of children?

...............................................................................................

...............................................................................................

...............................................................................................

...............................................................................................

# E.2.3 Carry out emergency procedures

| | Criteria | Knowledge evidence | Date completed |
|---|---|---|---|
| **PROGRESS CHECKLIST** | E.2.3.a | The importance of maintaining and using accurate records to enable parents to be contacted quickly if necessary. | |
| | E.2.3.b | Routine fire/emergency drill and how to respond promptly and appropriately in such situations. | |

## USEFUL BOOKS

*Caring for Young Children.* Jennie and Lance Lindon (1994) Macmillan.

E.2.3.a    Why is it important to maintain and use accurate records to contact parents in an emergency?

.........................................................................................................................................

.........................................................................................................................................

.........................................................................................................................................

.........................................................................................................................................

.........................................................................................................................................

.........................................................................................................................................

E.2.3.b    Describe the fire and emergency procedures that may be used in the work setting. State the work setting. Explain how the carers should react during the drill.

.........................................................................................................................................

.........................................................................................................................................

.........................................................................................................................................

.........................................................................................................................................

# E.2.4 Cope with accidents or injuries to children

<table>
<tr><td rowspan="9" style="writing-mode: vertical-rl">PROGRESS CHECKLIST</td><td>**Criteria**</td><td>**Knowledge evidence**</td><td>**Date completed**</td></tr>
<tr><td>E.2.4.a</td><td>Convey information to parents without causing undue alarm.</td><td></td></tr>
<tr><td>E.2.4.b</td><td>How to recognise and cope with children's emotional reaction to accidents and emergencies.</td><td></td></tr>
<tr><td>E.2.4.c</td><td>Suitable contents of first aid box for a child care/education setting and the importance of checking contents on a regular basis.</td><td></td></tr>
<tr><td>E.2.4.d</td><td>How to assess the situation quickly and decide if medical attention is required.</td><td></td></tr>
<tr><td>E.2.4.e</td><td>Basic First Aid required in an emergency and how to apply it.</td><td></td></tr>
<tr><td>E.2.4.f</td><td>The setting's requirements for recording accidents and emergencies.</td><td></td></tr>
<tr><td>E.2.4.g</td><td>The policies and procedures of the setting for handling and disposing of body fluids and waste material particularly in the light of AIDS/HIV virus, hepatitis etc.</td><td></td></tr>
<tr><td>E.2.4.h</td><td>The importance of carrying out standard procedures in the event of an accident in a calm and reassuring manner.</td><td></td></tr>
</table>

## USEFUL BOOKS

*First Aid for Children.* Sir Cameron Moffat (1994) Dorling Kindersley.

The British Red Cross and St. John's Ambulance service may also provide information specifically related to first aid and children.

| PORTFOLIO ACTIVITY SUMMARY | | 0–1 | 1–4 | 4–7 |
|---|---|---|---|---|
| **Criteria** | **Portfolio page reference** | | | |
| E.2.4.d&h | See page 134 for Portfolio Activity | | | |
| E.2.4.e | See page 134 for Portfolio Activity | | | |
| E.2.4.f | See page 134 for Portfolio Activity | | | |
| E.2.4.g | See page 134 for Portfolio Activity | | | |

E.2.4.a   How can the child care and education worker convey information to a parent without causing alarm?

..................................................................................................................................

..................................................................................................................................

..................................................................................................................................

..................................................................................................................................

E.2.4.b   A child can be emotionally upset if he/she is involved in an accident or emergency. How should the child care and education worker respond to the child?

..................................................................................................................................

..................................................................................................................................

..................................................................................................................................

..................................................................................................................................

E.2.4.c   List the contents of a First-Aid kit which may be used in the work setting.

..................................................................................................................................

..................................................................................................................................

..................................................................................................................................

Why is it important to check the contents of the First-Aid kit on a regular basis?

..............................................................................................................................................

..............................................................................................................................................

..............................................................................................................................................

..............................................................................................................................................

## E.2.4.d&h Portfolio Activity

*Write a short description of how you coped with a child who was injured in the work setting. Explain how effective you were in handling the situation and why it was important to remain calm and reassuring.*

## E.2.4.e Portfolio Activity

*Design an information sheet that could be displayed in the work setting highlighting the priorities for treating a casualty and how to apply them.*

## E.2.4.f Portfolio Activity

*Design an accident report form that could be used in the work setting.*

## E.2.4.g Portfolio Activity

*Describe the policies and procedures of the work setting for handling and disposing of body fluids and waste material.*

# E.2.5 Help to keep children safe from abuse

| | Criteria | Knowledge evidence | Date completed |
|---|---|---|---|
| **PROGRESS CHECKLIST** | E.2.5.a | The physical and emotional signs of physical abuse and neglect and sexual abuse in children. | |
| | E.2.5.b | The importance of adhering to regulations laid down in the setting with regard to suspected child abuse. | |
| | E.2.5.c | The boundaries of their role appropriate to the setting with regard to child abuse and understand the importance of informing line manager of explanations of injuries given by parent/carer. | |
| | E.2.5.d | The significance of negative changes in children's behaviour and the importance of observing, recording and reporting this. | |
| | E.2.5.e | The importance of involving parents/carers from the early stages of enquiries. | |
| | E.2.5.f | How to observe children while carrying out care routines for signs of injuries and abrasions and how and when these are reported. | |

## USEFUL BOOKS

*Special Issues in Child Care.* M. O'Hagan and M. Smith (1993) Bailliere Tindall.

E.2.5.a    List THREE different physical and THREE different emotional signs for EACH form of abuse:

(*a*) physical abuse;

.......................................................................................................................

.......................................................................................................................

(b) neglect;

...................................................................................................................

...................................................................................................................

(c) sexual abuse.

...................................................................................................................

...................................................................................................................

E.2.5.b    Why is it important to adhere to the work setting regulations on child protection?

...................................................................................................................

...................................................................................................................

...................................................................................................................

...................................................................................................................

...................................................................................................................

...................................................................................................................

E.2.5.c    Who should be the first person to be informed/consulted by a child care and education worker when child abuse is suspected?

...................................................................................................................

...................................................................................................................

E.2.5.d    Why is it important to observe, record and report unusual changes in a child's behaviour?

...................................................................................................................

...................................................................................................................

...................................................................................................................

...................................................................................................................

E.2.5.e    Should parents/carers be involved from the early stages of enquiries into alleged child abuse? Give reasons for your answer, discussing possible exceptions.

..................................................................................................................................

..................................................................................................................................

..................................................................................................................................

..................................................................................................................................

..................................................................................................................................

..................................................................................................................................

E.2.5.f    During the daily routine, when would the carer be able to identify possible signs of abuse?

..................................................................................................................................

..................................................................................................................................

..................................................................................................................................

..................................................................................................................................

# E.2.6 Ensure children's safety on outings

<table>
<tr><td rowspan="7" style="writing-mode:vertical-lr">PROGRESS CHECKLIST</td><td>**Criteria**</td><td>**Knowledge evidence**</td><td>**Date completed**</td></tr>
<tr><td>E.2.6.a</td><td>A range of outings suitable for individual age ranges.</td><td></td></tr>
<tr><td>E.2.6.b</td><td>The necessity of obtaining the permission of line manager before taking the children off the premises and when it is appropriate to obtain parental permission.</td><td></td></tr>
<tr><td>E.2.6.c</td><td>How to plan and prepare for an outing, with regard to safety, transport requirements, appropriate clothing, food and equipment.</td><td></td></tr>
<tr><td>E.2.6.d</td><td>The regulations including insurance cover regarding the safe transportation of children in private cars.</td><td></td></tr>
<tr><td>E.2.6.e</td><td>The importance of keeping a list of children on an outing and the necessity of checks at regular intervals.</td><td></td></tr>
<tr><td>E.2.6.f</td><td>The contribution parents can make to outings and the importance of giving them full information in advance of the event.</td><td></td></tr>
</table>

## USEFUL BOOKS

*Accident Prevention in Day Care and Play Settings.* Pam Laidman (1992) NES Arnold.

## PORTFOLIO ACTIVITY SUMMARY

| Criteria | Portfolio page reference | 0–1 | 1–4 | 4–7 |
|---|---|---|---|---|
| E.2.6.c | See page 139 for Portfolio Activity | | | |

E.2.6.a  List FIVE different locations which may be used as outings for EACH of the following age groups:

(*a*) 1–4 years;
(*b*) 4–7 years 11 months.

........................................................................................................................

........................................................................................................................

........................................................................................................................

........................................................................................................................

........................................................................................................................

E.2.6.b  Why is it important to gain the permission of the line manager before taking children on an outing?

........................................................................................................................

........................................................................................................................

Why is it important to gain parental permission?

........................................................................................................................

........................................................................................................................

### E.2.6.c *Portfolio Activity*

*Plan and, if possible, implement an outing for a child or group of children. The following should be included:*

(*a*) *safety;*
(*b*) *transport requirements;*
(*c*) *appropriate clothing;*
(*d*) *food;*
(*e*) *equipment;*
(*f*) *how the parents may be involved.*

E.2.6.d  What would the child care and education worker do to ensure the safety of a child while travelling in private transport? The legal requirements should be included.

..................................................................................................

..................................................................................................

..................................................................................................

..................................................................................................

..................................................................................................

..................................................................................................

E.2.6.e    Why is it important to keep a list of the children who are going on an outing?
Where should this list be kept?

..................................................................................................

..................................................................................................

..................................................................................................

..................................................................................................

E.2.6.f    Why is it valuable for parents to go on outings with children in the work
setting?

..................................................................................................

..................................................................................................

..................................................................................................

..................................................................................................

# P.2 ESTABLISH AND MAINTAIN RELATIONSHIPS WITH PARENTS OF YOUNG CHILDREN
## UNIT WIDE KNOWLEDGE

| | Criteria | Knowledge evidence | Date completed |
|---|---|---|---|
| **PROGRESS CHECKLIST** | P.2.a | The significance of the central role played by parents in their children's welfare and development. | |
| | P.2.b | The significance of the bond between parents and their children. | |
| | P.2.c | The social, environmental and cultural context in which families live. | |
| | P.2.d | Variations in family values and practices across cultural and other groupings and awareness that practices also vary within such groups. | |
| | P.2.e | How to communicate with parents as equals, how to listen to parents and how to adjust and modify communication with parents according to their interest, knowledge and confidence. | |
| | P.2.f | How pressure of parents' circumstances can affect their communication and relationships with their children and with other adults. | |
| | P.2.g | The importance of establishing positive relationships with parents including the possible barriers to communication and ways of overcoming these. | |
| | P.2.h | The principles of open communication and the limits and boundaries of confidentiality. | |
| | P.2.i | The candidate's role and responsibilities with regard to establishing and maintaining relationships with parents and circumstances in which parents should be referred to senior colleagues or other professionals. | |

# USEFUL BOOKS

*Caring for Young Children.* Jennie and Lance Lindon (1994) Macmillan.
*Special Issues in Child Care.* M. O'Hagan and M. Smith (1993) Bailliere Tindall.

| PORTFOLIO ACTIVITY SUMMARY | | | | |
|---|---|---|---|---|
| **Criteria** | **Portfolio page reference** | **0–1** | **1–4** | **4–7** |
| P.2.c | See page 143 for Portfolio Activity | | | |
| P.2.e | See page 144 for Portfolio Activity | | | |

# P.2 *Establish and maintain relationships with parents of young children*

P.2.a    Describe the role of the parents with regard to the child's welfare, education and development and explain why this role is so important?

..................................................................................................................................

..................................................................................................................................

..................................................................................................................................

..................................................................................................................................

..................................................................................................................................

..................................................................................................................................

P.2.b    Describe the bond which can exist between the parents and the child and explain why it is important to have this bond.

..................................................................................................................................

..................................................................................................................................

..................................................................................................................................

..................................................................................................................................

..................................................................................................................................

..................................................................................................................................

### P.2.c *Portfolio Activity*

*Describe the social, cultural and environmental situation of your work setting. Remember confidentiality must be maintained.*

P.2.d    Choose TWO different cultures and for EACH culture, describe the family values and practices.

..................................................................................................................................

..................................................................................................................

..................................................................................................................

..................................................................................................................

### P.2.e Portfolio Activity

*You have been asked to give a short talk (between 5 and 10 minutes) to student nursery nurses at the local college on how to communicate with and listen to parents. Write or tape the talk that you would give.*

P.2.f    Name THREE stressful situations that a parent might experience which could affect the relationship between the parent and the child.

..................................................................................................................

..................................................................................................................

..................................................................................................................

Describe how the child may be affected by EACH situation.

..................................................................................................................

..................................................................................................................

..................................................................................................................

P.2.g    Why is it important for the work setting to establish positive relationships with the parent?

..................................................................................................................

..................................................................................................................

..................................................................................................................

..................................................................................................................

What could prevent positive relationships being formed? Give TWO examples.

..................................................................................................................

..................................................................................................................

..................................................................................................................

..................................................................................................................

For EACH example, explain how the carer could help to build positive relationships.

..................................................................................................................

..................................................................................................................

..................................................................................................................

..................................................................................................................

P.2.h    Why is it important for the work setting to share information with the parents?

..................................................................................................................

..................................................................................................................

..................................................................................................................

..................................................................................................................

Why is it important for the work setting to maintain confidentiality?

..................................................................................................................

..................................................................................................................

..................................................................................................................

..................................................................................................................

P.2.i    Describe your role in establishing and maintaining good relationships with parents.

..................................................................................................................

..................................................................................................................

..................................................................................................................

...........................................................................................................

...........................................................................................................

...........................................................................................................

Describe TWO situations where you would ask for guidance from other professionals.

...........................................................................................................

...........................................................................................................

...........................................................................................................

...........................................................................................................

# P.2.1 Develop relationships with parents of young children

**PROGRESS CHECKLIST**

| Criteria | Knowledge evidence | Date completed |
|---|---|---|
| P.2.1.a | The concept and implications of shared care and partnership with parents. | |
| P.2.1.b | The kinds of information likely to be needed by parents. | |
| P.2.1.c | Methods of establishing relationships with parents who are not of the predominant cultural and linguistic group that the carer deals with, including sources of additional help and information. | |
| P.2.1.d | The policy of the setting concerning confidentiality of information including rules relating to children under Social Services/Work Supervision and medical records. | |
| P.2.1.e | Parents' rights under the relevant legislation. | |

## USEFUL BOOKS

*Caring for Young Children.* Jennie and Lance Lindon (1994) Macmillan.
*Special Issues in Child Care.* M. O'Hagan and M. Smith (1993) Bailliere Tindall.

## PORTFOLIO ACTIVITY SUMMARY

| Criteria | Portfolio page reference | 0–1 | 1–4 | 4–7 |
|---|---|---|---|---|
| P.2.1.d | See page 148 for Portfolio Activity | | | |

P.2.1.a    Why should the child care and education worker establish a good working relationship with the parent? What effect can a good working relationship have for the child AND parent?

..................................................................................................

..................................................................................................

..................................................................................................

..................................................................................................

..................................................................................................

..................................................................................................

**P.2.1.b**    List the kinds of information that may be needed by parents from the work
setting. Give FIVE examples.

..................................................................................................

..................................................................................................

..................................................................................................

..................................................................................................

..................................................................................................

**P.2.1.c**    Explain how the work setting can establish relationships with parents who are
not of the predominant cultural and linguistic group that the child care and
education worker deals with. Give details of where additional help and
information can be acquired.

..................................................................................................

..................................................................................................

..................................................................................................

..................................................................................................

..................................................................................................

..................................................................................................

## *P.2.1.d Portfolio Activity*

*Describe how the work setting ensures that information concerning the child and family remains
confidential at all times, except where a child may be at risk of abuse.*

P.2.1.e     Briefly describe the rights of parents under current legislation.

..................................................................................................................................

..................................................................................................................................

..................................................................................................................................

..................................................................................................................................

..................................................................................................................................

..................................................................................................................................

# P.2.2 Implement settling-in arrangements with parents

<table>
<tr><td rowspan="6" style="writing-mode: vertical-lr">PROGRESS CHECKLIST</td><td>**Criteria**</td><td>**Knowledge evidence**</td><td>**Date completed**</td></tr>
<tr><td>P.2.2.a</td><td>How children at different ages are likely to react to separation from parents and transition from one type of setting to another.</td><td></td></tr>
<tr><td>P.2.2.b</td><td>The arrangements for settling-in and how to communicate these to parents.</td><td></td></tr>
<tr><td>P.2.2.c</td><td>Differing theories about settling-in and separation from parents and their implications for practice.</td><td></td></tr>
<tr><td>P.2.2.d</td><td>Key areas on which clear policies and mutual agreement should be established e.g. routines, boundary setting, emergencies.</td><td></td></tr>
<tr><td>P.2.2.e</td><td>The difficulties faced by children and parents whose cultural and language background is different from the predominant culture and language of the setting.</td><td></td></tr>
</table>

## USEFUL BOOKS

*Working with Parents.* John Bastiani (1992) Routledge.
*Parental Involvement in Primary Schools.* Cyster, Cleft and Battle (eds) (1990) NFER.

P.2.2.a Explain how the following age groups of children may react when being separated from their parents or when settling into a new situation.

(*a*) 1–3 years 11 months

......................................................................................................................

......................................................................................................................

......................................................................................................................

......................................................................................................................

(*b*) 4–7 years 11 months

.........................................................................................

.........................................................................................

.........................................................................................

.........................................................................................

P.2.2.b    Describe TWO different ways in which the work setting can ensure that the settling-in period for the child AND the parents is as easy as possible.

.........................................................................................

.........................................................................................

.........................................................................................

.........................................................................................

.........................................................................................

.........................................................................................

P.2.2.c    Describe the theories behind good practice in settling children into a work setting and explain how these may have to be adapted to suit the parents/carer and/or individual needs.

.........................................................................................

.........................................................................................

.........................................................................................

.........................................................................................

.........................................................................................

.........................................................................................

.........................................................................................

.........................................................................................

P.2.2.d    List FIVE different rules and/or policies where the work setting and the
parents must cooperate with each other to ensure consistency and safety for
the child.

..................................................................................................................................

..................................................................................................................................

..................................................................................................................................

..................................................................................................................................

..................................................................................................................................

P.2.2.e    What difficulties do you think a child may have when settling into a new
setting, when his/her cultural and language background is different from that
of the majority of the group?

..................................................................................................................................

..................................................................................................................................

..................................................................................................................................

..................................................................................................................................

..................................................................................................................................

..................................................................................................................................

# P.2.3 Exchange information with parents about their children

<table>
<tr><th colspan="2" rowspan="7" style="writing-mode:vertical-lr">PROGRESS CHECKLIST</th></tr>
</table>

| | Criteria | Knowledge evidence | Date completed |
|---|---|---|---|
| **PROGRESS CHECKLIST** | P.2.3.a | Why exchange of information is beneficial to parents, children and staff. | |
| | P.2.3.b | The types of information needed from parents and how to obtain it, record it and keep it up to date. | |
| | P.2.3.c | The types of information needed by parents and how to communicate it effectively. | |
| | P.2.3.d | Strategies for sharing and exchange of information which take account of the need for flexibility and sensitive negotiation with parents. | |
| | P.2.3.e | Barriers to effective communication. | |
| | P.2.3.f | How to keep records of information, confidential nature of some information and who has access to records. | |

## USEFUL BOOKS

*Working with Parents.* John Bastiani (1992) Routledge.

## PORTFOLIO ACTIVITY SUMMARY

| Criteria | Portfolio page reference | 0–1 | 1–4 | 4–7 |
|---|---|---|---|---|
| P.2.3.b | See page 154 for Portfolio Activity | | | |
| P.2.3.c | See page 154 for Portfolio Activity | | | |
| P.2.3.d | See page 154 for Portfolio Activity | | | |
| P.2.3.f | See page 154 for Portfolio Activity | | | |

P.2.3.a    Why is it important to exchange information with the parents?

....................................................................................................................................

....................................................................................................................................

....................................................................................................................................

....................................................................................................................................

....................................................................................................................................

....................................................................................................................................

 ### *P.2.3.b Portfolio Activity*

*Collect evidence of the types of information required by the work setting from the parents. This should include the way in which the information is obtained, how it is recorded and how it is kept up to date.*

 ### *P.2.3.c Portfolio Activity*

*Collect evidence of the types of information required by the parents and how the work setting communicates it to the parents.*

 ### *P.2.3.d Portfolio Activity*

*Explain how the work setting shares and exchanges sensitive information with the parents.*

P.2.3.e    List FIVE factors which could prevent information being passed on to the parents.

....................................................................................................................................

....................................................................................................................................

....................................................................................................................................

....................................................................................................................................

....................................................................................................................................

 ### *P.2.3.f Portfolio Activity*

*Describe how the work setting keeps confidential information and who has access to it.*

# P.2.4 Share the care and management of children with their parents

<table>
<tr><th>PROGRESS CHECKLIST</th><th>Criteria</th><th>Knowledge evidence</th><th>Date completed</th></tr>
<tr><td></td><td>P.2.4.a</td><td>The worker's role in the care and management of children and in sharing this with parents.</td><td></td></tr>
<tr><td></td><td>P.2.4.b</td><td>The central role of parents in the care and management of their child(ren).</td><td></td></tr>
<tr><td></td><td>P.2.4.c</td><td>Rationale for policies pursued by setting and ways in which family values may differ from those of the setting.</td><td></td></tr>
<tr><td></td><td>P.2.4.d</td><td>Health and safety procedures with regard to different types of emergencies including accidents, illness, emergency closure of the setting etc. and when and how to contact parents.</td><td></td></tr>
</table>

## USEFUL BOOKS

*Accident Prevention in Day Care and Play Settings.* Pam Laidman (1992) NES Arnold.
*Special Issues in Child Care.* M. O'Hagan and M. Smith (1993) Bailliere Tindall.

| PORTFOLIO ACTIVITY SUMMARY | | | | |
|---|---|---|---|---|
| Criteria | Portfolio page reference | 0–1 | 1–4 | 4–7 |
| P.2.4.c | See page 156 for Portfolio Activity | | | |
| P.2.4.d | See page 156 for Portfolio Activity | | | |

P.2.4.a      Describe the child care and education worker's role in sharing the care of the child with the parents.

..................................................................................................

..................................................................................................

..................................................................................................

P.2.4.b   Describe the role of the parent in the care and management of the child.

..................................................................................................

..................................................................................................

..................................................................................................

..................................................................................................

 ### P.2.4.c Portfolio Activity

*Describe one policy that has been adopted by the work setting in relation to the care and education of the child. Explain why this policy is used and how it may differ from that used by the parents.*

### P.2.4.d Portfolio Activity

*Design an information leaflet for parents which explains the health and safety procedures for THREE different types of emergencies, e.g. accidents, illness, 'pick up' arrangements, poor weather conditions etc.*

# C.12 FEED BABIES
## UNIT WIDE KNOWLEDGE

PROGRESS CHECKLIST

| Criteria | Knowledge evidence | Date completed |
|---|---|---|
| C.12.a | A basic knowledge of the growth and development of babies up to 12 months and how this can be affected by the social, emotional and physical environment. | |
| C.12.b | A general basic knowledge of the nutritional requirements of babies up to 12 months. | |
| C.12.c | The importance of hygiene and how to maintain standards of hygiene acceptable to the setting. | |
| C.12.d | Cultural variations and approaches to feeding and weaning babies. | |
| C.12.e | Range of equipment available and its appropriate use. | |

## USEFUL BOOKS

*Babies and Young Children Book 1 Development 0–7 years.* Beaver, *et al.* (1994) Stanley Thornes.

## PORTFOLIO ACTIVITY SUMMARY

| Criteria | Portfolio page reference | 0–1 | 1–4 | 4–7 |
|---|---|---|---|---|
| C.12.a&e | See page 158 for Portfolio Activity | | | |
| C.12.b | See page 158 for Portfolio Activity | | | |

### C.12.a&e Portfolio Activity

*Design a booklet for parents which explains how a baby grows and develops from birth to 12 months. The booklet should explain how the baby's development is affected by the social, emotional and physical environment. Examples of equipment and how to use it should be also be included.*

 ### C.12.b Portfolio Activity

*Design a poster or leaflet for parents which explains the nutritional requirements of a baby up to 12 months old.*

C.12.c     Why is it important to ensure that the work setting is hygienic?

..........................................................................................................................................

..........................................................................................................................................

..........................................................................................................................................

..........................................................................................................................................

..........................................................................................................................................

..........................................................................................................................................

C.12.d     Choose TWO different cultures. For EACH culture, briefly describe how babies are fed and weaned.

..........................................................................................................................................

..........................................................................................................................................

..........................................................................................................................................

..........................................................................................................................................

..........................................................................................................................................

..........................................................................................................................................

# C.12.1 Sterilise feeding equipment

| PROGRESS CHECKLIST | Criteria | Knowledge evidence | Date completed |
|---|---|---|---|
| | C.12.1.a | The principles of sterilisation and different methods of sterilisation. | |
| | C.12.1.b | The differences between sterilisation and social cleanliness. | |
| | C.12.c | Different methods of cleaning feeding equipment. | |

## USEFUL BOOKS

*Child Care and Development.* Pamela Minnett (1994) John Murray.

## PORTFOLIO ACTIVITY SUMMARY

| Criteria | Portfolio page reference | 0–1 | 1–4 | 4–7 |
|---|---|---|---|---|
| C.12.1.a | See below for Portfolio Activity | | | |

 ### C.12.1.a Portfolio Activity

*Design a chart or leaflet which explains the importance of sterilisation. The chart should include:*

(*a*) *the importance of sterilisation;*
(*b*) *how bacteria and infections are spread;*
(*c*) *the possible effects of not sterilising feeding equipment.*

C.12.1.a    Describe THREE different methods of sterilisation.

..............................................................................................................................................

..............................................................................................................................................

..............................................................................................................................................

..............................................................................................................................................

..............................................................................................................................................

..............................................................................................................

..............................................................................................................

..............................................................................................................

..............................................................................................................

..............................................................................................................

..............................................................................................................

..............................................................................................................

C.12.1.b    What is the difference between sterilisation and social cleanliness?

..............................................................................................................

..............................................................................................................

..............................................................................................................

..............................................................................................................

..............................................................................................................

..............................................................................................................

C.12.1.c    Describe TWO different methods of cleaning feeding equipment, other than
sterilisation.

..............................................................................................................

..............................................................................................................

..............................................................................................................

..............................................................................................................

..............................................................................................................

..............................................................................................................

..............................................................................................................

# C.12.2 Make up formula feeds for babies

<table>
<tr><td rowspan="6" style="vertical-align:middle">PROGRESS CHECKLIST</td><td>Criteria</td><td>Knowledge evidence</td><td>Date completed</td></tr>
<tr><td>C.12.2.a</td><td>The typical feeding requirements of babies at different stages.</td><td></td></tr>
<tr><td>C.12.2.b</td><td>The different types of milk required for cultural, religious or medical reasons.</td><td></td></tr>
<tr><td>C.12.2.c</td><td>The storage properties of made up feeds.</td><td></td></tr>
<tr><td>C.12.2.d</td><td>The adverse effects if feeds are not properly made up.</td><td></td></tr>
<tr><td>C.12.2.e</td><td>Different methods of heating made up feeds.</td><td></td></tr>
</table>

## USEFUL BOOKS

*Babies and Young Children Book 1 Development 0–7 years.* Beaver, *et al.* (1994) Stanley Thornes.
*Caring for Young Children.* Jennie and Lance Lindon (1994) Macmillan.

C.12.2.a    What are the feeding requirements of a baby under 4 months of age?

..................................................................................................................................

..................................................................................................................................

..................................................................................................................................

..................................................................................................................................

..................................................................................................................................

..................................................................................................................................

What are the feeding requirements of a baby over 4 months of age?

..................................................................................................................................

..................................................................................................................

..................................................................................................................

..................................................................................................................

..................................................................................................................

..................................................................................................................

**C.12.2.b**   Describe the different types of milk that may be required for:

(*a*) cultural reasons;

..................................................................................................................

..................................................................................................................

(*b*) medical reasons.

..................................................................................................................

..................................................................................................................

**C.12.2.c**   How should formula feeds be stored?

..................................................................................................................

..................................................................................................................

..................................................................................................................

..................................................................................................................

..................................................................................................................

..................................................................................................................

A carer has bought a manufactured formula feed. How long can it safely be kept for before being used?

..................................................................................................................

..................................................................................................................

..........................................................................................................................................................

..........................................................................................................................................................

A baby has not eaten a full portion of the formula food that has been prepared. If this food is stored, what precautions should be taken to ensure that the food is safe to eat at a later stage?

..........................................................................................................................................................

..........................................................................................................................................................

..........................................................................................................................................................

..........................................................................................................................................................

..........................................................................................................................................................

..........................................................................................................................................................

C.12.2.d    What could happen if the formula feed is not prepared properly?

..........................................................................................................................................................

..........................................................................................................................................................

..........................................................................................................................................................

..........................................................................................................................................................

..........................................................................................................................................................

..........................................................................................................................................................

C.12.2.e    Describe TWO different ways of preparing formula feeds.

..........................................................................................................................................................

..........................................................................................................................................................

..........................................................................................................................................................

..........................................................................................................................................................

..........................................................................................................................................................

# C.12.3 Bottle feed a baby

| Criteria | Knowledge evidence | Date completed |
|----------|--------------------|----------------|
| C.12.3.a | Typical patterns of feeding for babies of different stages and how they may vary. | |
| C.12.3.b | Why some babies may have difficulties with feeding and how to overcome common difficulties. | |
| C.12.3.c | Specialised equipment for babies with special needs and how and where to obtain it. | |
| C.12.3.d | The importance of interaction/communication with babies before, during and after feeding. | |
| C.12.3.e | The importance of a suitable environment for feeding. | |
| C.12.3.f | The importance of winding and settling the baby after feeds and how this contributes to the baby's welfare. | |
| C.12.3.g | Dangers and problems associated with feeds. | |

## USEFUL BOOKS

*Babies and Young Children Book 1 Development 0–7 years.* Beaver, *et al.* (1994) Stanley Thornes.

| PORTFOLIO ACTIVITY SUMMARY | | | | |
|----------|--------------------------|-----|-----|-----|
| Criteria | Portfolio page reference | 0–1 | 1–4 | 4–7 |
| C.12.3.a | See page 165 for Portfolio Activity | | | |
| C.12.3.a | See page 165 for Portfolio Activity | | | |

### C.12.3.a Portfolio Activity

*Design a leaflet for parents which explains how to bottle feed a baby under 4 months of age.*

### C.12.3.a Portfolio Activity

*Plan and implement, if appropriate, a routine for feeding a baby over 4 months of age.*

C.12.3.a    Describe the differences between the feeding patterns of a baby under 4 months and a baby over 4 months of age.

..................................................................................................................................

..................................................................................................................................

..................................................................................................................................

..................................................................................................................................

..................................................................................................................................

..................................................................................................................................

C.12.3.b    Why do some babies have difficulty feeding? How can the carer overcome these difficulties?

..................................................................................................................................

..................................................................................................................................

..................................................................................................................................

..................................................................................................................................

..................................................................................................................................

..................................................................................................................................

C.12.3.c    A baby with special needs may require specialised feeding equipment. Give examples of the type of equipment that may be necessary. Where could parents obtain the equipment from?

..................................................................................................................................

....................................................................................................

....................................................................................................

....................................................................................................

....................................................................................................

....................................................................................................

**C.12.3.d**    Why is it important for the carer to talk to the baby before, during and after the baby has been fed?

....................................................................................................

....................................................................................................

....................................................................................................

....................................................................................................

....................................................................................................

**C.12.3.e**    Where should the baby be fed? Give reasons for your choice.

....................................................................................................

....................................................................................................

....................................................................................................

....................................................................................................

....................................................................................................

**C.12.3.f**    Why is it important to wind and settle the baby after the feed? How does this contribute to the baby's welfare?

....................................................................................................

....................................................................................................

..................................................................................................................................

..................................................................................................................................

..................................................................................................................................

..................................................................................................................................

C.12.3.g    Describe the dangers and problems associated with feeds.

..................................................................................................................................

..................................................................................................................................

..................................................................................................................................

..................................................................................................................................

..................................................................................................................................

..................................................................................................................................

# C.12.4 Spoon feed a baby

| | Criteria | Knowledge evidence | Date completed |
|---|---|---|---|
| **PROGRESS CHECKLIST** | C.12.4.a | The process of weaning and current medical advice on when weaning should be started. | |
| | C.12.4.b | Methods of food preparation and associated hygiene and safety requirements. | |
| | C.12.4.c | What constitutes a balanced diet for babies of different ages and how and when to introduce new foods. | |
| | C.12.4.d | The importance of consultation between parents and the other carers over feeding routines. | |
| | C.12.4.e | Babies' need to experiment with feeds and feed themselves as part of growing independence. | |
| | C.12.4.f | Relevance of vitamin supplements. | |

## USEFUL BOOKS

*Babies and Young Children Book 1 Development 0–7 years.* Beaver, *et al.* (1994) Stanley Thornes.

## PORTFOLIO ACTIVITY SUMMARY

| Criteria | Portfolio page reference | 0–1 | 1–4 | 4–7 |
|---|---|---|---|---|
| C.12.4.a | See page 169 for Portfolio Activity | | | |
| C.12.4.c | See page 170 for Portfolio Activity | | | |

## *C.12.4.a Portfolio Activity*

*Design a chart which shows how weaning on to solid food may progress. The following information should be included:*

      (*a*) *age of baby;*
      (*b*) *nutritional requirements;*
      (*c*) *type of food;*
      (*d*) *taste and texture of food.*

C.12.4.a    When should a baby be weaned? Give reasons for your answer.

..................................................................................................................................

..................................................................................................................................

..................................................................................................................................

..................................................................................................................................

..................................................................................................................................

..................................................................................................................................

C.12.4.b    Select THREE different types of food which may be given to a baby. Describe how EACH food should be prepared for a spoon feed.

..................................................................................................................................

..................................................................................................................................

..................................................................................................................................

..................................................................................................................................

..................................................................................................................................

..................................................................................................................................

..................................................................................................................................

..................................................................................................................................

..................................................................................................................................

What health and safety requirements should be taken into account when preparing the foods?

.................................................................................................................................

.................................................................................................................................

.................................................................................................................................

.................................................................................................................................

.................................................................................................................................

.................................................................................................................................

## C.12.4.c Portfolio Activity

*Plan and implement, if appropriate, a balanced menu for one day for a 6-month-old baby AND a 12-month-old baby.*

C.12.4.d   Why is it important for the carer to discuss the feeding routines of the baby with the parents?

.................................................................................................................................

.................................................................................................................................

.................................................................................................................................

.................................................................................................................................

.................................................................................................................................

C.12.4.e   Describe ways in which the carer can encourage the baby to eat independently.

.................................................................................................................................

.................................................................................................................................

.................................................................................................................................

.................................................................................................................................

..................................................................................................

..................................................................................................

**C.12.4.f**    How and when should vitamin supplements be used when feeding a baby?

..................................................................................................

..................................................................................................

..................................................................................................

..................................................................................................

..................................................................................................

..................................................................................................

# C.13 CARE FOR BABIES
## UNIT WIDE KNOWLEDGE

| Criteria | Knowledge evidence | Date completed |
|----------|--------------------|----------------|
| C.13.a | A basic knowledge of the growth and development of babies up to 12 months and how this can be affected by the social, emotional and physical environment. | |
| C.13.b | The needs and requirements of young babies in relation to physical care and how these needs can be met. | |
| C.13.c | Effective ways of handling babies both for safety and for encouraging interaction. | |
| C.13.d | The way that caring for babies may vary with different cultures. | |
| C.13.e | The importance of communication and stimulation to the development of babies up to 12 months. | |
| C.13.f | The importance of a safe, clean environment for babies. | |

## USEFUL BOOKS

*Babies and Young Children Book 1 Development 0–7 years.* Beaver, *et al.* (1994) Stanley Thornes.

## PORTFOLIO ACTIVITY SUMMARY

| Criteria | Portfolio page reference | 0–1 | 1–4 | 4–7 |
|----------|--------------------------|-----|-----|-----|
| C.13.a | See page 173 for Portfolio Activity | | | |
| C.13.c | See page 173 for Portfolio Activity | | | |

# *C.13 Care for babies*

## *C.13.a Portfolio Activity*

*Design a booklet for parents which explains how a baby grows and develops from birth to 12 months. The booklet should explain how the baby's development is affected by the social, emotional and physical environment. (**NB** You may have completed this work for C.12.a.)*

C.13.b    What physical care does a baby need?

.............................................................................................................

.............................................................................................................

.............................................................................................................

.............................................................................................................

.............................................................................................................

.............................................................................................................

How can these needs be met?

.............................................................................................................

.............................................................................................................

.............................................................................................................

.............................................................................................................

.............................................................................................................

.............................................................................................................

## *C.13.c Portfolio Activity*

*Design a poster for the work setting which explains how to handle babies. It should highlight safety and ways to encourage interaction between the adult and the child.*

C.13.d    Select TWO different cultures and briefly describe how EACH culture cares for its babies.

...................................................................................................

...................................................................................................

...................................................................................................

...................................................................................................

...................................................................................................

...................................................................................................

**C.13.e**    Why is it important for the adult to communicate with and stimulate the baby?

...................................................................................................

...................................................................................................

...................................................................................................

...................................................................................................

...................................................................................................

...................................................................................................

**C.13.f**    Why is it important to ensure that the work setting is safe and clean?

...................................................................................................

...................................................................................................

...................................................................................................

...................................................................................................

...................................................................................................

...................................................................................................

# *C.13.1 Give a baby a bath*

| | Criteria | Knowledge evidence | Date completed |
|---|---|---|---|
| **PROGRESS CHECKLIST** | C.13.1.a | The general health and safety requirements of babies at different ages up to 12 months. | |
| | C.13.1.b | Why different parts of the baby's body are bathed differently. | |
| | C.13.1.c | Why particular attention should be paid to creases and folds in the skin. | |
| | C.13.1.d | Health and safety procedures necessary to protect the worker from infection and how to use them. | |
| | C.13.1.e | Possible unusual conditions and reactions which should be reported. | |
| | C.13.1.f | The importance of bathtime as a sensory and pleasurable experience for babies. | |
| | C.13.1.g | How babies react to water at different ages and their individual differences and experiences. | |
| | C.13.1.h | The range and suitability of bathing equipment and toiletries. | |

## USEFUL BOOKS

*Babies and Young Children Book 1 Development 0–7 years.* Beaver, *et al.* (1994) Stanley Thornes.

## PORTFOLIO ACTIVITY SUMMARY

| Criteria | Portfolio page reference | 0–1 | 1–4 | 4–7 |
|----------|--------------------------|-----|-----|-----|
| C.13.1.d | See page 177 for Portfolio Activity | | | |
| C.13.1.f | See page 178 for Portfolio Activity | | | |

C.13.1.a    Describe the health and safety requirements of babies aged between:

(*a*) birth and 4 weeks;

.....................................................................................................................................

.....................................................................................................................................

.....................................................................................................................................

(*b*) 1 month and 3 months;

.....................................................................................................................................

.....................................................................................................................................

.....................................................................................................................................

(*c*) 4 months and 6 months;

.....................................................................................................................................

.....................................................................................................................................

.....................................................................................................................................

(*d*) 6 months and 1 year.

.....................................................................................................................................

.....................................................................................................................................

.....................................................................................................................................

C.13.1.b    Explain why different parts of the baby's body are bathed separately:

...........................................................................................................................

...........................................................................................................................

...........................................................................................................................

...........................................................................................................................

...........................................................................................................................

...........................................................................................................................

C.13.1.c    Why is it particularly important to wash the creases and folds in a baby's skin?

...........................................................................................................................

...........................................................................................................................

...........................................................................................................................

...........................................................................................................................

...........................................................................................................................

...........................................................................................................................

## C.13.1.d Portfolio Activity

*Design a poster which explains to carers how to protect themselves from infection when working with babies.*

C.13.1.e    Describe an unusual condition or reaction from a baby during bathtime which should be reported by the carer.

...........................................................................................................................

...........................................................................................................................

...........................................................................................................................

...........................................................................................................................

..................................................................................................................................

..................................................................................................................................

C.13.1.f    Why is it important to make bathtime a pleasurable experience for babies?

..................................................................................................................................

..................................................................................................................................

..................................................................................................................................

..................................................................................................................................

..................................................................................................................................

..................................................................................................................................

What other pleasures can a baby get from bathtime?

..................................................................................................................................

..................................................................................................................................

..................................................................................................................................

..................................................................................................................................

..................................................................................................................................

 ### *C.13.1.f Portfolio Activity*

*Observe a baby aged between birth and 6 months having a bath. Describe how the baby reacted to the water.*

*Observe a baby aged between 6 months and one year having a bath. Describe how the baby reacted to the water. Compare his/her reactions with your observations of the younger baby.*

*Design a leaflet which shows a range of bathing equipment and toiletries. Write short notes to explain the suitability of the equipment.*

# C.13.2 Change nappies and dress a baby

| PROGRESS CHECKLIST | Criteria | Knowledge evidence | Date completed |
|---|---|---|---|
| | C.13.2.a | The common skin conditions and variations in bowel and bladder action which need to be reported. | |
| | C.13.2.b | The emotional issues around toilet training and when and how it should be introduced. | |
| | C.13.2.c | Cultural differences in toileting and hygiene procedures. | |
| | C.13.2.d | Different types of nappies and how to apply them according to age and gender of the baby. | |
| | C.13.2.e | The range and suitability of clothing. | |
| | C.13.2.f | Awareness of the requirement to change nappy. | |
| | C.13.2.g | Range, application and suitability of toiletries. | |

## USEFUL BOOKS

*Caring for Young Children.* Jennie and Lance Lindon (1994) Macmillan.

| PORTFOLIO ACTIVITY SUMMARY | | | | |
|---|---|---|---|---|
| Criteria | Portfolio page reference | 0–1 | 1–4 | 4–7 |
| C.13.2.g | See page 182 for Portfolio Activity | | | |

C.13.2.a    Name and describe a skin condition which may be observed when changing a baby's nappy.

.......................................................................................................................................

.......................................................................................................................................

...........................................................................................

...........................................................................................

Describe any variations in bowel and/or bladder action which may need to be reported by the carer.

...........................................................................................

...........................................................................................

...........................................................................................

...........................................................................................

...........................................................................................

...........................................................................................

C.13.2.b    How and when should toilet training be introduced?

...........................................................................................

...........................................................................................

...........................................................................................

...........................................................................................

...........................................................................................

...........................................................................................

What emotional issues could be experienced during this time?

...........................................................................................

...........................................................................................

...........................................................................................

...........................................................................................

...........................................................................................

Describe the cultural differences which may occur in toilet training and hygiene procedures.

..................................................................................................................................

..................................................................................................................................

..................................................................................................................................

..................................................................................................................................

..................................................................................................................................

..................................................................................................................................

C.13.2.d    Describe the different types of nappies that are available and explain how to use them.

..................................................................................................................................

..................................................................................................................................

..................................................................................................................................

..................................................................................................................................

C.13.2.e    Describe the range and suitability of clothing for a baby aged between birth and 12 months.

..................................................................................................................................

..................................................................................................................................

..................................................................................................................................

..................................................................................................................................

..................................................................................................................................

..................................................................................................................................

..................................................................................................................................

..................................................................................................................................

C.13.2.f    Why is it important to change a baby's nappy regularly?

..............................................................................................................................................

..............................................................................................................................................

..............................................................................................................................................

..............................................................................................................................................

..............................................................................................................................................

..............................................................................................................................................

## C.13.2.g Portfolio Activity

*Design a leaflet for parents which shows the range and suitability of toiletries for a baby. Brief instructions should be given on how to use the toiletries.*

# C.13.3 Stimulate babies to encourage their development

| | Criteria | Knowledge evidence | Date completed |
|---|---|---|---|
| **PROGRESS CHECKLIST** | C.13.3.a | Appropriate toys and equipment to stimulate babies from 0–12 months. | |
| | C.13.3.b | The importance of all the senses in stimulating development. | |
| | C.13.3.c | When and how to provide appropriate assistance to encourage walking. | |
| | C.13.3.d | Suitable safety equipment for use with babies of different ages and stages of development. | |
| | C.13.3.e | Awareness of limitations of stimulation. | |

## USEFUL BOOKS

*Babies and Young Children Book 1 Development 0–7 years.* Beaver, *et al.* (1994) Stanley Thornes.

C.13.3.a   You have been asked by a parent to recommend a selection of toys that would be suitable for a baby during the first year of his/her life. What would you suggest and why?

.........................................................................................................................

.........................................................................................................................

.........................................................................................................................

.........................................................................................................................

.........................................................................................................................

.........................................................................................................................

C.13.3.b    Why is it important to develop the senses of a baby?

..................................................................................................................................

..................................................................................................................................

..................................................................................................................................

..................................................................................................................................

..................................................................................................................................

..................................................................................................................................

C.13.3.c    When and how should the carer encourage a baby to walk?

..................................................................................................................................

..................................................................................................................................

..................................................................................................................................

..................................................................................................................................

..................................................................................................................................

..................................................................................................................................

C.13.3.d    What safety equipment could you buy for:

(*a*) a cooker; ......................................................................................................................

(*b*) electric sockets; .........................................................................................................

(*c*) a bath; ........................................................................................................................

(*d*) doors and cupboards ...............................................................................................

C.13.3.e    What effect could lack of stimulation have on a baby?

..................................................................................................................................

..................................................................................................................................

..................................................................................................................................

..................................................................................................................................

..................................................................................................................................

..................................................................................................................................

# C.13.4 Clean and maintain clothing and nursery equipment

<table>
<tr><td rowspan="6" style="writing-mode: vertical-rl">PROGRESS CHECKLIST</td><td>**Criteria**</td><td>**Knowledge evidence**</td><td>**Date completed**</td></tr>
<tr><td>C.13.4.a</td><td>The importance of maintaining standards of hygiene and cleanliness for clothing and nursery equipment for babies at different stages.</td><td></td></tr>
<tr><td>C.13.4.b</td><td>Cleaning and disinfectant materials suitable for baby clothing and nursery equipment and how to use them safely.</td><td></td></tr>
<tr><td>C.13.4.c</td><td>Appropriate laundry methods/techniques for different types of materials.</td><td></td></tr>
<tr><td>C.13.4.d</td><td>Simple repair techniques.</td><td></td></tr>
</table>

## USEFUL BOOKS

*Babies and Young Children Book 1 Development 0–7 years.* Beaver, *et al.* (1994) Stanley Thornes.

C.13.4.a     Why is it important to ensure that a baby's clothes are clean and hygienic?

.................................................................................................................................

.................................................................................................................................

.................................................................................................................................

.................................................................................................................................

.................................................................................................................................

.................................................................................................................................

C.13.4.b    Complete the table below:

| | Cleaning materials | Disinfectants | How to use them |
|---|---|---|---|
| 1 | | | |
| 2 | | | |
| 3 | | | |
| 4 | | | |
| 5 | | | |

C.13.4.c    How would you wash the following materials?

(a) wool;

.................................................................................................................

.................................................................................................................

(b) cotton;

.................................................................................................................

.................................................................................................................

(c) nylon.

.................................................................................................................

.................................................................................................................

C.13.4.d    A button has become loose on a baby's jumper. How should this be repaired? Why is it important to repair it?

.................................................................................................................

.................................................................................................................

.................................................................................................................

.................................................................................................................

A baby's wooden brick has splintered. How should this be repaired?

........................................................................................................................................

........................................................................................................................................

........................................................................................................................................

........................................................................................................................................

# M.1 GIVE ADMINISTRATIVE AND TECHNICAL SUPPORT ON REQUEST

## *M.1.1 Set up technical equipment for use*

| | Criteria | Knowledge evidence | Date completed |
|---|---|---|---|
| **P R O G R E S S   C H E C K L I S T** | M.1.1.a | Operating procedures and safety requirements of the setting regarding use of equipment. | |
| | M.1.1.b | How to use equipment following manufacturers' instructions. | |
| | M.1.1.c | The procedures of the setting for dealing with faults in equipment. | |
| | M.1.1.d | Accessories and spare parts required for different types of equipment. | |

## USEFUL BOOKS

Please refer to the manufacturer's instruction books for each type of equipment.

## PORTFOLIO ACTIVITY SUMMARY

| Criteria | Portfolio page reference | 0–1 | 1–4 | 4–7 |
|---|---|---|---|---|
| M.1.1.a | See page 189 for Portfolio Activity | | | |
| M.1.1.b | See page 189 for Portfolio Activity | | | |

### M.1.1.a Portfolio Activity

*Design a booklet for staff in the work setting which explains the operating procedures AND safety requirements for EACH of the following pieces of equipment:*

> (*a*) *cassette recorder/player;*
> (*b*) *video recorder/player;*
> (*c*) *overhead projector;*
> (*d*) *slide projector;*
> (*e*) *computer;*
> (*f*) *science equipment.*

### M.1.1.b Portfolio Activity

*Set up EACH of the pieces of equipment given in M.1.1.a according to the manufacturer's instructions. Describe how effective you were.*

M.1.1.c   Describe the procedures used by the work setting for reporting AND dealing with faults to equipment.

.......................................................................................................................................

.......................................................................................................................................

.......................................................................................................................................

.......................................................................................................................................

.......................................................................................................................................

M.1.1.d   For EACH of the pieces of equipment named in M.1.1.a provide a list of accessories and spare parts that may be required.

.......................................................................................................................................

.......................................................................................................................................

.......................................................................................................................................

.......................................................................................................................................

.......................................................................................................................................

# *M.1.2 Prepare copies of papers*

| | Criteria | Knowledge evidence | Date completed |
|---|---|---|---|
| **PROGRESS CHECKLIST** | M.1.2.a | How to operate equipment. | |
| | M.1.2.b | What to do if equipment breaks down. | |
| | M.1.2.c | Copyright requirements. | |

## USEFUL BOOKS

Please refer to the manufacturer's instruction books for each type of equipment.

M.1.2.a    Describe how to operate reprographic equipment.

......................................................................................................................

......................................................................................................................

......................................................................................................................

......................................................................................................................

......................................................................................................................

M.1.2.b    Explain the procedures used in the work setting when the reprographic
equipment breaks down.

......................................................................................................................

......................................................................................................................

......................................................................................................................

......................................................................................................................

......................................................................................................................

M.1.2.c    Briefly describe the legal requirements concerning copyright.

..............................................................................................................................

..............................................................................................................................

..............................................................................................................................

..............................................................................................................................

..............................................................................................................................

# M.1.3 Prepare sets of materials

| Criteria | Knowledge evidence | Date completed |
|---|---|---|
| M.1.3.a | Different methods of preparation for different types of materials. | |

## USEFUL BOOKS

Your mentor/tutor should have details of appropriate material on this subject.

| PORTFOLIO ACTIVITY SUMMARY | | | | |
|---|---|---|---|---|
| Criteria | Portfolio page reference | 0–1 | 1–4 | 4–7 |
| M.1.3.a | See below for Portfolio Activity | | | |

 ### M.1.3.a Portfolio Activity

*In your portfolio explain how each of the following materials should be prepared for use by a child.*

(a) *Art and craft materials:*
- *paints (different types of paints should be included);*
- *glue and paste;*
- *clay;*
- *paper (different types of paper and their purpose, should be included);*
- *collage materials.*

(b) *Play and learning materials:*
- *sand;*
- *water;*
- *wood;*
- *dough.*

(**NB** *Other materials, not mentioned above, may be included in the portfolio.*)

# M.1.4 Monitor stock levels

<table>
<tr><td rowspan="5">PROGRESS CHECKLIST</td><td>Criteria</td><td>Knowledge evidence</td><td>Date completed</td></tr>
<tr><td>M.1.4.a</td><td>How to record stock levels.</td><td></td></tr>
<tr><td>M.1.4.b</td><td>The procedures of the setting for dealing with shortfalls in materials.</td><td></td></tr>
<tr><td>M.1.4.c</td><td>Health and safety requirements of the setting for storage and use of materials.</td><td></td></tr>
<tr><td>M.1.4.d</td><td>Materials which may deteriorate and how to prevent or delay this.</td><td></td></tr>
</table>

## USEFUL BOOKS

Your mentor/tutor should have details of appropriate material on this subject.

## PORTFOLIO ACTIVITY SUMMARY

| Criteria | Portfolio page reference | 0–1 | 1–4 | 4–7 |
|---|---|---|---|---|
| M.1.4.a | See below for Portfolio Activity | | | |
| M.1.4.b | See page 194 for Portfolio Activity | | | |

### M.1.4.a Portfolio Activity

*Design one or more checklists which may be used in the work setting to record the stock levels of the following equipment:*

> (a) *art and craft materials;*
> (b) *cleaning materials;*
> (c) *stationery.*

**M.1.4.b Portfolio Activity**

*Describe the procedures used in the work setting when there are insufficient materials available for use.*

M.1.4.c    From the list given in M.1.3.a, select TWO materials from (*a*) and TWO materials from (*b*). Describe the health and safety requirements for the storage AND use of EACH of the materials.

..........................................................................................................................................

..........................................................................................................................................

..........................................................................................................................................

..........................................................................................................................................

..........................................................................................................................................

..........................................................................................................................................

..........................................................................................................................................

..........................................................................................................................................

..........................................................................................................................................

..........................................................................................................................................

M.1.4.d    From the list given in M.1.3.a, list the materials which will deteriorate and explain how the deterioration of EACH material may be delayed or prevented.

..........................................................................................................................................

..........................................................................................................................................

..........................................................................................................................................

..........................................................................................................................................

..........................................................................................................................................

..........................................................................................................................................

..........................................................................................................................................

..........................................................................................................................................

..........................................................................................................................................

..........................................................................................................................................

# M.3 Work under the direction of others
## Unit wide knowledge

| Criteria | Knowledge evidence | Date completed |
|---|---|---|
| M.3.a | What good practice is according to the setting. | |
| M.3.b | The aims of and objectives of the organisation. | |
| M.3.c | The structure of the organisation including line management. | |
| M.3.d | The candidate's own role and that of others with whom he/she works closely. | |
| M.3.e | The importance of fulfilling commitments given in the work situation. | |
| M.3.f | A basic awareness of how teams work. | |
| M.3.g | The importance of self-awareness. | |
| M.3.h | Their responsibility to seek assistance, further training or resources to improve current practice. | |
| M.3.i | The Equal Opportunities Code of Practice and its importance. | |
| M.3.j | The importance of keeping to the boundaries of confidentiality as appropriate to the setting. | |
| M.3.k | The importance of relating positively to others. | |
| M.3.l | The importance of open communication, both positive and negative. | |

# USEFUL BOOKS

*Special Issues in Child Care.* M. O'Hagan and M. Smith (1993) Bailliere Tindall.

| PORTFOLIO ACTIVITY SUMMARY | | | | |
|---|---|---|---|---|
| **Criteria** | **Portfolio page reference** | **0–1** | **1–4** | **4–7** |
| M.3.a,b, c,d&i | See page 197 for Portfolio Activity | | | |
| M.3.f | See page 197 for Portfolio Activity | | | |

# M.3 Work under the direction of others

## M.3.a,b,c,d&i Portfolio Activity

*Design a booklet for parents which includes the following information about the work setting:*

    (a) *the aims and objectives of the organisation;*
    (b) *the structure of the organisation including the line management;*
    (c) *the role of members of staff, including your own;*
    (d) *the Equal Opportunities Code of Practice and its importance;*
    (e) *what is meant by 'good practice'.*

M.3.e    Why is it important to carry out tasks that you have been asked to do by other staff, promptly and efficiently?

.......................................................................................................................

.......................................................................................................................

.......................................................................................................................

.......................................................................................................................

.......................................................................................................................

.......................................................................................................................

.......................................................................................................................

## M.3.f Portfolio Activity

*Observe two or more adults in the work setting. Describe how they work as a team.*

M.3.g    Why is self-awareness important?

.......................................................................................................................

.......................................................................................................................

.......................................................................................................................

.......................................................................................................................

M.3.h    'I have spent a lot of time getting my qualification. I do not need to learn any more.' What advice would you give to this adult?

..................................................................................................................

..................................................................................................................

..................................................................................................................

..................................................................................................................

..................................................................................................................

..................................................................................................................

M.3.j    Why is it important to maintain confidentiality in the work setting?

..................................................................................................................

..................................................................................................................

..................................................................................................................

M.3.k    Why is it important to respond positively to others?

..................................................................................................................

..................................................................................................................

..................................................................................................................

..................................................................................................................

M.3.l    Why is it important to share information within the work setting?

..................................................................................................................

..................................................................................................................

..................................................................................................................

..................................................................................................................

# M.3.1 Carry out work allocated

| | Criteria | Knowledge evidence | Date completed |
|---|---|---|---|
| **PROGRESS CHECKLIST** | M.3.1.a | The importance of listening and recording information accurately. | |
| | M.3.1.b | The importance of carrying out instructions as specified. | |
| | M.3.1.c | The importance of prioritising and managing time efficiently. | |
| | M.3.1.d | The Health and Safety Policy specific to the setting. | |

## USEFUL BOOKS

*Special Issues in Child Care.* M. O'Hagan and M. Smith (1993) Bailliere Tindall.
*The Manager's Handbook.* A. Young (1987) Sphere.

M.3.1.a     Why is it important to listen to and record information accurately?

...................................................................................................................

...................................................................................................................

...................................................................................................................

...................................................................................................................

...................................................................................................................

...................................................................................................................

M.3.1.b     Why is it important for the child care and education worker to carry out instructions given by another member of staff accurately?

...................................................................................................................

...................................................................................................................

...................................................................................................

...................................................................................................

...................................................................................................

...................................................................................................

Why is it important for the child care and education worker to carry out instructions given by a parent accurately?

...................................................................................................

...................................................................................................

...................................................................................................

...................................................................................................

**M.3.1.c**    Why is it important to prioritise and manage time efficiently?

...................................................................................................

...................................................................................................

...................................................................................................

...................................................................................................

**M.3.1.d**    Briefly outline the Health and Safety Policy in the work setting.

...................................................................................................

...................................................................................................

...................................................................................................

...................................................................................................

# M.3.2 Give feedback on work carried out

| Criteria | Knowledge evidence | Date completed |
|---|---|---|
| M.3.2.a | The daily/weekly routine of the setting. | |
| M.3.2.b | The importance of showing sensitivity to the special needs of the child and family. | |
| M.3.2.c | Planning and recording within the candidate's own area of responsibility. | |
| M.3.2.d | How the work of the organisation relates to, and is constrained by, external agencies. | |

*(PROGRESS CHECKLIST)*

## USEFUL BOOKS

*A Curriculum for the Pre-school Child.* Audrey Curtis (1986) NFER Nelson.

## PORTFOLIO ACTIVITY SUMMARY

| Criteria | Portfolio page reference | 0–1 | 1–4 | 4–7 |
|---|---|---|---|---|
| M.3.2.a | See below for Portfolio Activity | | | |
| M.3.2.d | See page 202 for Portfolio Activity | | | |

## M.3.2.a Portfolio Activity

*Describe, in detail, the daily routine AND the weekly routine of the work setting. This should include the routines for the parents, children and staff.*

M.3.2.b    Why is it important to be sensitive towards children with special needs and their parents?

.......................................................................................................................................................

.......................................................................................................................................................

..................................................................................................

..................................................................................................

M.3.2.c     Why should the child care and education worker plan and record the daily
            and weekly routine of the work setting?

..................................................................................................

..................................................................................................

..................................................................................................

..................................................................................................

## M.3.2.d *Portfolio Activity*

*Design a chart which shows the roles and responsibilities of the workers within the work setting.
External agencies should also be included.*

# M.3.3 Relate to colleagues in the work setting

| | Criteria | Knowledge evidence | Date completed |
|---|---|---|---|
| **PROGRESS CHECKLIST** | M.3.3.a | Ways of dealing with conflict situations in a positive manner. | |
| | M.3.3.b | Grievance/complaints procedures and how to use them. | |

## USEFUL BOOKS

*Special Issues in Child Care.* M. O'Hagan and M. Smith (1993) Bailliere Tindall.

| PORTFOLIO ACTIVITY SUMMARY | | | | |
|---|---|---|---|---|
| Criteria | Portfolio page reference | 0–1 | 1–4 | 4–7 |
| M.3.3.a | See below for Portfolio Activity | | | |

## M.3.3.a Portfolio Activity

*Observe a member of staff handling a situation which has caused conflict. Explain how the member of staff handled the situation in a positive manner.*

M.3.3.b    Briefly outline the grievance and complaints procedure of the work setting and explain how a child care and education worker could use them.

........................................................................................................

........................................................................................................

........................................................................................................

........................................................................................................

........................................................................................................

........................................................................................................

# P.9 WORK WITH PARENTS IN A GROUP FOR YOUNG CHILDREN
## UNIT WIDE KNOWLEDGE

| | Criteria | Knowledge evidence | Date completed |
|---|---|---|---|
| **PROGRESS CHECKLIST** | P.9.a | The operation of different aspects of the group. | |
| | P.9.b | How to communicate with parents as equals and how to listen to parents. | |
| | P.9.c | The variety of contributions parents can make to the work of the group and understand some parents' reluctance or inability to become involved. | |
| | P.9.d | The benefits to the group, the parents and the children of parents' involvement in the group. | |
| | P.9.e | The social, environmental and cultural context in which local families live. | |
| | P.9.f | How family lifestyles, approaches to childrearing and play vary with family background and culture. | |

## USEFUL BOOKS

*Working Towards Partnership in the Early Years.* Gillian Pugh and Erica De'ath (1989) National Children's Bureau.
*Working with Young Children (Part Four).* Jennie Laishley (1987) Hodder and Stoughton.

| PORTFOLIO ACTIVITY SUMMARY | | | | |
|---|---|---|---|---|
| Criteria | Portfolio page reference | 0–1 | 1–4 | 4–7 |
| P.9.b | See page 205 for Portfolio Activity | | | |

# P.9 Work with parents in a group for young children

P.9.a        Describe the operation of THREE different aspects of the group.

..................................................................................................................................

..................................................................................................................................

..................................................................................................................................

..................................................................................................................................

..................................................................................................................................

..................................................................................................................................

## P.9.b Portfolio Activity

*You have been asked to give a short talk (between 5 and 10 minutes) to student nursery nurses at the local college on how to communicate with and listen to parents. Write or tape the talk that you would give. (**NB**  You may have answered this question in P.2.e.)*

P.9.c        Describe THREE ways in which parents can become involved in the work of the group.

..................................................................................................................................

..................................................................................................................................

..................................................................................................................................

..................................................................................................................................

..................................................................................................................................

..................................................................................................................................

Why are some parents reluctant to become involved in the work of the group?

..................................................................................................................................

..................................................................................................................................

..............................................................................................................

..............................................................................................................

**P.9.d**     What are the benefits of parents becoming involved in the work of the group?

..............................................................................................................

..............................................................................................................

..............................................................................................................

..............................................................................................................

**P.9.e**     Describe the social, cultural and environmental situation of your work setting. Confidentiality must be maintained.
(***NB*** *You may have answered this question in* P.2.c.)

..............................................................................................................

..............................................................................................................

..............................................................................................................

..............................................................................................................

..............................................................................................................

..............................................................................................................

**P.9.f**     Choose TWO different cultures and describe the family lifestyles, including play and child rearing.

..............................................................................................................

..............................................................................................................

..............................................................................................................

..............................................................................................................

..............................................................................................................

..............................................................................................................

## *P.9.1 Explain operation of group to parents*

<table>
<tr><td rowspan="3" style="writing-mode:vertical-lr">PROGRESS CHECKLIST</td><td>**Criteria**</td><td>**Knowledge evidence**</td><td>**Date completed**</td></tr>
<tr><td>P.9.1.a</td><td>Sources of help in the case of communication difficulties.</td><td></td></tr>
<tr><td>P.9.1.b</td><td>The boundaries of responsibility for work with parents and to whom enquiries beyond these should be referred.</td><td></td></tr>
</table>

## USEFUL BOOKS

*Working Towards Partnership in the Early Years.* Gillian Pugh and Erica De'ath (1989) National Children's Bureau.

P.9.1.a   A parent with a severe hearing impairment has a child in the work setting. What help can the work setting give to ensure that the parent has all the necessary information about the work setting?

..................................................................................................................

..................................................................................................................

..................................................................................................................

..................................................................................................................

..................................................................................................................

..................................................................................................................

A parent, whose home language is not that of the carer, requires information about the work setting. How can the work setting ensure that the parent receives and understands the information?

..................................................................................................................

..................................................................................................................

..................................................................................................................

..........................................................................................

..........................................................................................

..........................................................................................

P.9.1.b    Describe the responsibilities that different members of staff have when
           working with parents, e.g. pre-school leader, parent helper, trainee etc.

..........................................................................................

..........................................................................................

..........................................................................................

..........................................................................................

..........................................................................................

..........................................................................................

           Who should staff go to for help if the situation is beyond their responsibility?

..........................................................................................

..........................................................................................

..........................................................................................

..........................................................................................

..........................................................................................

..........................................................................................

# P.9.2 Help parents to participate in the functions of the group

| | Criteria | Knowledge evidence | Date completed |
|---|---|---|---|
| **PROGRESS CHECKLIST** | P.9.2.a | Possible barriers to parents' participation in the group. | |
| | P.9.2.b | Ways in which parents' skills can help the group. | |

## USEFUL BOOKS

*Working Towards Partnership in the Early Years.* Gillian Pugh and Erica De'ath (1989) National Children's Bureau.
*Working with Young Children (Part Four).* Jennie Laishley (1987) Hodder and Stoughton.

P.9.2.a    What factors could prevent parents participating in the work of the setting?

.........................................................................................................................................

.........................................................................................................................................

.........................................................................................................................................

.........................................................................................................................................

.........................................................................................................................................

.........................................................................................................................................

P.9.2.b    Parents have skills which can be of value to the work setting. List FIVE ways in which parents may be able to contribute to the work of the setting.

.........................................................................................................................................

.........................................................................................................................................

.........................................................................................................................................

.........................................................................................................................................

.........................................................................................................................................

# P.9.3 Encourage parents to participate in activities with children

| | Criteria | Knowledge evidence | Date completed |
|---|---|---|---|
| **PROGRESS CHECKLIST** | P.9.3.a | The nature and purpose of children's activities. | |
| | P.9.3.b | Different ways of stimulating parents' interest in children's activities. | |
| | P.9.3.c | The ways in which parents can participate in children's activities. | |
| | P.9.3.d | The reasons why some parents are reluctant to participate in children's activities. | |

## USEFUL BOOKS

*Working Towards Partnership in the Early Years.* Gillian Pugh and Erica De'ath (1989) National Children's Bureau.
*Working with Young Children (Part Four).* Jennie Laishley (1987) Hodder and Stoughton.

| PORTFOLIO ACTIVITY SUMMARY | | | | |
|---|---|---|---|---|
| Criteria | Portfolio page reference | 0–1 | 1–4 | 4–7 |
| P.9.3.a&c | See below for Portfolio Activity | | | |
| P.9.3.b | See page 211 for Portfolio Activity | | | |

### P.9.3.a&c Portfolio Activity

*Design a booklet for parents which includes the following information:*

    (*a*) *the activities that are available to the children in the work setting and the way in which the activities promote the development of the child;*

    (*b*) *practical ways in which the parents can participate in the children's activities.*

### *P.9.3.b Portfolio Activity*

*Select THREE activities from the booklet. For EACH activity, describe ways of stimulating the parents' interest in the children's activities.*

P.9.3.d    Why do some parents find it difficult to participate in the children's activities? Your answer should relate to real situations wherever possible. Confidentiality must be maintained at all times.

..................................................................................................................................................

..................................................................................................................................................

..................................................................................................................................................

..................................................................................................................................................

..................................................................................................................................................

..................................................................................................................................................

# M.2 Carry out the administration of the provision for a care/education setting Unit wide knowledge

| PROGRESS CHECKLIST | Criteria | Knowledge evidence | Date completed |
|---|---|---|---|
| | M.2.a | A basic understanding of methods of keeping records. | |
| | M.2.b | The policies and procedures of the setting concerning authorisation of expenditure. | |

## Useful books

*Getting to Know You.* Lynne Bartholomew and Tina Bruce (1993) Hodder and Stoughton.

# M.2 Carry out the administration of the provision for a care/education setting

M.2.a       Describe different methods of keeping records. Examples could be included in your portfolio.

..........................................................................................................................

..........................................................................................................................

..........................................................................................................................

..........................................................................................................................

..........................................................................................................................

..........................................................................................................................

..........................................................................................................................

..........................................................................................................................

..........................................................................................................................

..........................................................................................................................

M.2.b       Briefly describe the policies and procedures of the work setting regarding the authorisation of expenditure.

..........................................................................................................................

..........................................................................................................................

..........................................................................................................................

..........................................................................................................................

..........................................................................................................................

..........................................................................................................................

..........................................................................................................................

..........................................................................................................................

..........................................................................................................................

# M.2.1 Receive and disburse monies

| PROGRESS CHECKLIST | Criteria | Knowledge evidence | Date completed |
|---|---|---|---|
| | M.2.1.a | Methods of keeping records of income and expenditure. | |
| | M.2.1.b | The candidate's role in relation to the policies and procedures of the setting concerning:<br>i) authorisation of expenditure;<br>ii) flexibility about families' payments. | |

## USEFUL BOOKS

*The Manager's Handbook.* A. Young (1987) Sphere.

| PORTFOLIO ACTIVITY SUMMARY | | | | |
|---|---|---|---|---|
| Criteria | Portfolio page reference | 0–1 | 1–4 | 4–7 |
| M.2.1.a | See below for Portfolio Activity | | | |

 ### M.2.1.a Portfolio Activity

*Provide examples of different methods of recording the income and expenditure for the work setting. The records should include:*

> (*a*) *weekly payments;*
> (*b*) *monthly payments;*
> (*c*) *annual payments;*
> (*d*) *regular payments;*
> (*e*) *occasional payments;*
>
> *The methods of payment should be noted e.g. cash, cheque etc.*

M.2.1.b   Who gives permission in the work setting, for the following:

(*a*) salaries?

(*b*) small daily payments?

..................................................................................................................................

(*c*) large equipment and/or materials?

..................................................................................................................................

Describe the procedures used in the work setting when a parent is unable to make appropriate payments.

..................................................................................................................................

..................................................................................................................................

..................................................................................................................................

..................................................................................................................................

..................................................................................................................................

..................................................................................................................................

..................................................................................................................................

..................................................................................................................................

# M.2.2 Implement admission procedures

| | Criteria | Knowledge evidence | Date completed |
|---|---|---|---|
| PROGRESS CHECKLIST | M.2.2.a | Admissions policies of the setting. | |
| | M.2.2.b | Candidate's role in relation to admissions. | |
| | M.2.2.c | Information required about children and families. | |
| | M.2.2.d | Information to give to parents. | |
| | M.2.2.e | Settling-in arrangements. | |

## USEFUL BOOKS

*Special Issues in Child Care.* M O'Hagan and M. Smith (1993) Bailliere Tindall.

| PORTFOLIO ACTIVITY SUMMARY | | | | |
|---|---|---|---|---|
| Criteria | Portfolio page reference | 0–1 | 1–4 | 4–7 |
| M.2.2.a | See below for Portfolio Activity | | | |
| M.2.2.d | See page 217 for Portfolio Activity | | | |
| M.2.2.e | See page 217 for Portfolio Activity | | | |

## M.2.2.a Portfolio Activity

*Describe the admissions policy of the work setting.*

M.2.2.b    Describe your role in the admissions policy of the work setting.

..............................................................................................................................................

..............................................................................................................................................

..........................................................................................

..........................................................................................

..........................................................................................

..........................................................................................

M.2.2.c    What information does the child care and education worker need to know
about the child and the family in the work setting? Give reasons for your
answer.

..........................................................................................

..........................................................................................

..........................................................................................

..........................................................................................

..........................................................................................

..........................................................................................

 ### *M.2.2.d Portfolio Activity*

*Design a leaflet which gives the necessary information to parents for a child who is about to be
admitted to the work setting.*

M.2.2.d    What information do parents require from the work setting after the child has
been admitted?

..........................................................................................

..........................................................................................

..........................................................................................

..........................................................................................

 ### *M.2.2.e Portfolio Activity*

*Design a leaflet for parents which explains the settling-in arrangements for a new child.*

# M.2.3 Maintain records of information

| PROGRESS CHECKLIST | Criteria | Knowledge evidence | Date completed |
|---|---|---|---|
| | M.2.3.a | Methods of keeping records. | |
| | M.2.3.b | The requirements of the registering authority for records. | |
| | M.2.3.c | The policies of the setting concerning confidentiality. | |
| | M.2.3.d | Information needed in an emergency. | |

## USEFUL BOOKS

*Getting to Know You.* Lynne Bartholomew and Tina Bruce (1993) Hodder and Stoughton.

| PORTFOLIO ACTIVITY SUMMARY | | | | |
|---|---|---|---|---|
| Criteria | Portfolio page reference | 0–1 | 1–4 | 4–7 |
| M.2.3.a | See below for Portfolio Activity | | | |

 ### M.2.3.a Portfolio Activity

*Collect samples of different methods of keeping records. These may include attendance records, accident records, children's records.*

M.2.3.b    What records are required by the Social Service Department from pre-school groups?

.............................................................................................................................

.............................................................................................................................

.............................................................................................................................

.......................................................................................................

.......................................................................................................

.......................................................................................................

M.2.3.c    Describe the work setting's procedures on confidentiality.

.......................................................................................................

.......................................................................................................

.......................................................................................................

.......................................................................................................

M.2.3.d    Describe the information which may be needed in an emergency.

.......................................................................................................

.......................................................................................................

.......................................................................................................

.......................................................................................................

# M.2.4 Operate budgets

| | Criteria | Knowledge evidence | Date completed |
|---|---|---|---|
| PROGRESS CHECKLIST | M.2.4.a | How to record expenditure against budget limits. | |

## USEFUL BOOKS

*The Manager's Handbook.* A. Young (1987) Sphere.

| PORTFOLIO ACTIVITY SUMMARY | | | | |
|---|---|---|---|---|
| Criteria | Portfolio page reference | 0–1 | 1–4 | 4–7 |
| M.2.4.a | See below for Portfolio Activity | | | |

 ### M.2.4.a Portfolio Activity

*Provide samples of recording the income and expenditure of the pre-school group.*

# M.2.5 Operate systems for the supply of materials and equipment

<table>
<tr><td rowspan="6" style="writing-mode: vertical-rl">PROGRESS CHECKLIST</td><td>**Criteria**</td><td>**Knowledge evidence**</td><td>**Date completed**</td></tr>
<tr><td>M.2.5.a</td><td>The procedures of the setting concerning ordering/hiring equipment and materials.</td><td></td></tr>
<tr><td>M.2.5.b</td><td>Suitable suppliers of relevant equipment and materials.</td><td></td></tr>
<tr><td>M.2.5.c</td><td>How to record stock levels.</td><td></td></tr>
<tr><td>M.2.5.d</td><td>How to maintain simple inventories of equipment.</td><td></td></tr>
<tr><td>M.2.5.e</td><td>Suitable and safe methods of storing different types of materials.</td><td></td></tr>
</table>

## USEFUL BOOKS

Your mentor/tutor should have details of appropriate material on this subject

## PORTFOLIO ACTIVITY SUMMARY

| Criteria | Portfolio page reference | 0–1 | 1–4 | 4–7 |
|---|---|---|---|---|
| M.2.5.c&d | See page 222 for Portfolio Activity | | | |
| M.2.5.e | See page 222 for Portfolio Activity | | | |

M.2.5.a    Describe how the work setting orders and/or hires equipment and materials.

......................................................................................................................................

......................................................................................................................................

......................................................................................................................................

......................................................................................................................................

.......................................................................................................................

.......................................................................................................................

M.2.5.b    Provide a list of suitable suppliers for equipment and materials. Give reasons
for your choice.

.......................................................................................................................

.......................................................................................................................

.......................................................................................................................

.......................................................................................................................

.......................................................................................................................

.......................................................................................................................

## M.2.5.c & d Portfolio page

*Provide samples of recording stock levels in the work setting and explain how a check is maintained on the equipment.*

## M.2.5.e Portfolio Activity

*Design a poster which could be used in the store cupboard which explains how to store different types of materials in a safe and appropriate way.*

# M.20 Work with/to a management committee
## Unit wide knowledge

| | Criteria | Knowledge evidence | Date completed |
|---|---|---|---|
| **PROGRESS CHECKLIST** | M.20.a | The structure, role and policies of the organisation. | |
| | M.20.b | The roles and areas of responsibility of committee and self. | |
| | M.20.c | The purpose of a contract of employment, grievance procedures and job remit. | |
| | M.20.d | The nature of confidentiality and its boundaries. | |

## Useful books

It may be useful to contact the Pre-school Learning Alliance or other similar organisations for appropriate information.

# M.20 Work with/to a management committee

M.20.a    Describe the structure, role and the policies of the organisation.
(**NB** *You may have answered this question in* M.3.a.)

.......................................................................................................................

.......................................................................................................................

.......................................................................................................................

.......................................................................................................................

.......................................................................................................................

.......................................................................................................................

.......................................................................................................................

.......................................................................................................................

.......................................................................................................................

.......................................................................................................................

.......................................................................................................................

M.20.b    Name the committee(s) that the organisation works with/to. Describe the
roles and areas of responsibility that the committee(s) has/have.

.......................................................................................................................

.......................................................................................................................

.......................................................................................................................

.......................................................................................................................

.......................................................................................................................

.......................................................................................................................

...........................................................................................................

...........................................................................................................

...........................................................................................................

...........................................................................................................

...........................................................................................................

...........................................................................................................

Describe your role on the committee.

...........................................................................................................

...........................................................................................................

...........................................................................................................

...........................................................................................................

M.20.c    Describe the purpose of the following:

(*a*) contract of employment;

...........................................................................................................

...........................................................................................................

...........................................................................................................

...........................................................................................................

(*b*) grievance procedure;

...........................................................................................................

...........................................................................................................

...........................................................................................................

...........................................................................................................

(*c*) job description.

...........................................................................................................

.........................................................................................

.........................................................................................

.........................................................................................

**M.20.d**    Why is it important to maintain confidentiality in the work setting?

.........................................................................................

.........................................................................................

.........................................................................................

.........................................................................................

.........................................................................................

.........................................................................................

.........................................................................................

.........................................................................................

# M.20.1 *Report to a management committee*

<table>
<tr><td rowspan="7" style="writing-mode:vertical-rl">PROGRESS CHECKLIST</td></tr>
<tr><th>Criteria</th><th>Knowledge evidence</th><th>Date completed</th></tr>
<tr><td>M.20.1.a</td><td>The nature and purpose of the report and the implications for the way information is presented.</td><td></td></tr>
<tr><td>M.20.1.b</td><td>The principles of meetings and the procedures adopted by the local committee.</td><td></td></tr>
<tr><td>M.20.1.c</td><td>The equipment, supplies and other resources required for the running of the group.</td><td></td></tr>
<tr><td>M.20.1.d</td><td>The importance of providing accurate information in enabling management committees to function effectively.</td><td></td></tr>
<tr><td>M.20.1.e</td><td>The policy of the setting concerning confidentiality.</td><td></td></tr>
</table>

## USEFUL BOOKS

*The Manager's Handbook.* A. Young (1989) Sphere.

## PORTFOLIO ACTIVITY SUMMARY

| Criteria | Portfolio page reference | 0–1 | 1–4 | 4–7 |
|----------|--------------------------|-----|-----|-----|
| M.20.1.a | See page 228 for Portfolio Activity | | | |
| M.20.1.b | See page 228 for Portfolio Activity | | | |

## M.20.1.a Portfolio Activity

*Collect a sample of different types of reports used in the pre-school group, eg reports on equipment and other resources, college student reports etc. Using the sample, copy and complete the table below.*

| Name of report | Purpose of report | Person(s) who completes it | Who is the report for? | How often is it completed? |
| --- | --- | --- | --- | --- |
|  |  |  |  |  |

## M.20.1.b Portfolio Activity

*Select one meeting that has taken place recently with the management committee. Explain:*

> (a) *the aim of the meeting;*
> (b) *the procedures of the meeting.*

> *It may be appropriate to include a copy of the agenda, minutes of the previous meeting, papers submitted and any other relevant information.*

M.20.1.c    You have been asked to set up a pre-school group in a local hall. Make a list of the equipment, supplies and other resources that would be required for the group.

........................................................................................................................

........................................................................................................................

........................................................................................................................

........................................................................................................................

........................................................................................................................

........................................................................................................................

........................................................................................................................

........................................................................................................................

........................................................................................................................

..................................................................................................

..................................................................................................

..................................................................................................

**M.20.1.d**  Why is it important to provide accurate information to the management
committee of a group?

..................................................................................................

..................................................................................................

..................................................................................................

..................................................................................................

..................................................................................................

..................................................................................................

**M.20.1.e**  Describe the policy of the pre-school group concerning confidentiality.

..................................................................................................

..................................................................................................

..................................................................................................

..................................................................................................

..................................................................................................

..................................................................................................

..................................................................................................

..................................................................................................

..................................................................................................

..................................................................................................

..................................................................................................

# M.20.2 Prepare plans for the management committee

<table>
<tr><td rowspan="9" style="writing-mode: vertical-lr">PROGRESS CHECKLIST</td><td>Criteria</td><td>Knowledge evidence</td><td>Date completed</td></tr>
<tr><td>M.20.2.a</td><td>The purpose of planning in the effective running of a pre-school group.</td><td></td></tr>
<tr><td>M.20.2.b</td><td>How to prepare short/long term and sessional plans.</td><td></td></tr>
<tr><td>M.20.2.c</td><td>Possible resources for use by the group and understand their potential and limitations.</td><td></td></tr>
<tr><td>M.20.2.d</td><td>The different types of development of children (physical, social, emotional, intellectual, sensory and language).</td><td></td></tr>
<tr><td>M.20.2.e</td><td>The equipment and materials required to cater for each type of development.</td><td></td></tr>
<tr><td>M.20.2.f</td><td>The relationship between types of activities and experiences and aspects of children's development and learning.</td><td></td></tr>
<tr><td>M.20.2.g</td><td>The importance and use of variation in the types of activity and variation in the way activities are presented for stimulating children's interest and enjoyment.</td><td></td></tr>
</table>

## USEFUL BOOKS

*Planning for Early Learning.* Victoria Hurst (1991) Paul Chapman Publishing.

| PORTFOLIO ACTIVITY SUMMARY | | | | |
|---|---|---|---|---|
| Criteria | Portfolio page reference | 0–1 | 1–4 | 4–7 |
| M.20.2.b, c,d,e&f | See page 231 for Portfolio Activity | | | |

M.20.2.a   Why is it important for child care and education workers to plan the work they are going to do with the children?

..............................................................................................................................

..............................................................................................................................

..............................................................................................................................

..............................................................................................................................

..............................................................................................................................

..............................................................................................................................

..............................................................................................................................

..............................................................................................................................

### *M.20.2.b,c,d,e&f Portfolio Activity*

*Provide examples of the following plans that have been used in the pre-school group:*

> (*a*)  *short-term plans e.g. daily, weekly, monthly;*
> (*b*)  *long-term plans e.g. termly, yearly;*
> (*c*)  *plans for special events e.g. festivals, open days etc.*

> *The plans should include: equipment, materials, furniture etc.; staffing, if appropriate; and how the activities will encourage the all round development of the child.*

M.20.2.g   Why is it important to vary the activities that are presented to the children?

..............................................................................................................................

..............................................................................................................................

..............................................................................................................................

..............................................................................................................................

..............................................................................................................................

..............................................................................................................................

# M.20.3 Carry out instructions/policy of the management committee

| | Criteria | Knowledge evidence | Date completed |
|---|---|---|---|
| **PROGRESS CHECKLIST** | M.20.3.a | Boundaries of responsibility in relation to children in the group, parents and management committee and areas where there may be a conflict of interest. | |
| | M.20.3.b | The importance of feedback and suggestions in contributing to effective policy making. | |
| | M.20.3.c | The role of training in personal and professional development. | |

## USEFUL BOOKS

*The Manager's Handbook.* A. Young (1987) Sphere.

M.20.3.a    While the group is functioning, who has responsibility for:

(*a*) the individual child;

.................................................................................................................

.................................................................................................................

.................................................................................................................

.................................................................................................................

(*b*) the whole group.

.................................................................................................................

.................................................................................................................

.................................................................................................................

.................................................................................................................

(**NB** *There may be more than one answer.*)

Describe any areas of conflict which may exist in relation to who has responsibility.

..........................................................................................

..........................................................................................

..........................................................................................

..........................................................................................

..........................................................................................

..........................................................................................

M.20.3.b   Why is it important to provide feedback and to give suggestions when deciding on future policies of the work setting?

..........................................................................................

..........................................................................................

..........................................................................................

..........................................................................................

..........................................................................................

..........................................................................................

M.20.3.c   Why is personal training and development important for child care and education workers working with young children?

..........................................................................................

..........................................................................................

..........................................................................................

..........................................................................................

..........................................................................................

..........................................................................................

Which organisations provide training for the child care and education worker?

..........................................................................................................................

..........................................................................................................................

..........................................................................................................................

..........................................................................................................................

..........................................................................................................................

..........................................................................................................................